CROSSWORDS

CROSSWORDS

OVER 100 PUZZLES

ARCTURUS

ARCTURUS

© Arcturus Holdings Limited
Puzzles © 2013 by Puzzle Press Ltd

ISBN 978-1-4351-4973-1

Manufactured in Malaysia

2   4   6   8   10 9   7   5   3

Introduction

There are 125 crossword puzzles in this volume, which is a lot of solving time! To make sure your hours are spent pleasantly, we've loaded them with snappy themes, clever wordplay, humorous clues, and more fun than you can shake a pencil at. You'll find references to movies, books, history, sports, music, geography, and many more areas of human knowledge. It's like having the world at your fingertips, but in puzzle form.

In addition to touching on a wide range of subjects, we've also created these crosswords to span the generations. Don't be surprised to see contemporary British pop superstar ADELE crossing ELVIS Presley in a grid!

Note that the puzzles in this book do not indicate when an answer consists of more than one word. So an answer like ICED TEA will simply be clued as "Summer drink" without any hint that there are two separate words in the entry. Keep an eye out for these multiword answers, which can be tricky to spot!

People often ask: what should I do if I get stuck on a puzzle? I always give them three pieces of advice:

1) Get up and get a drink of water or walk around for a couple of minutes, then return to the puzzle. Seeing the clues again with fresh eyes may trigger a vital answer.

2) Say a tough clue out loud to yourself, since hearing it may jog your brain in different ways than reading it.

3) Cheat! Look up one or two critical answers in the back of the book and write them in. The rest of the answers might then gush out like water through a burst dam.

The other question they ask is: should I be solving in pencil or pen? The answer, of course, is: whichever you prefer, as long as you're having fun! Which I hope you will with the puzzles in this book.

Levi Davis

1

Pretty Cheesy

Across

1 Enjoys the pool
6 Wrapped item
10 Mac
13 Words said while smacking your forehead
14 Namesakes of a Gilbert and Sullivan princess
15 Former Israeli prime minister Olmert
17 Prank where you pour seasoning over the captain of the football team?
19 Review on Yelp, e.g.
20 "___ the DJ, I'm the Rapper" (1988 album)
21 "There's ___ in the bottom of the sea"
22 Orchestra instrument
23 ___-ball (arcade rolling game)
24 Danced ungracefully
26 ___ of Liberty
29 Update the decor
30 Get ready for a bodybuilding competition
31 Area where everything feels like a Utah city?
36 Big street: abbr.
37 Historic French town (anagram of LUCY N.)
38 Icelandic band Sigur ___ (hidden in GROSS)
39 Rampart for rebels?
42 Typeface units
44 Food for pigs
45 Letter-shaped house
46 Jeer toward a play's villain
49 "Star ___" (William Shatner show)
50 History Channel show that follows loggers in the Pacific Northwest
51 Condescend
53 Org. that fined over a "wardrobe malfunction"
56 Construction beam
57 Emile's lesser known author brother?
59 Seaweed, in sushi bars
60 It's under a toddler's Band-Aid
61 Minnesotan's neighbor
62 Pale
63 Dollar bills
64 Former Israeli prime minister Meir

Down

1 Jr., last year
2 "This is fun!"
3 Little devils
4 Treasure hunt need
5 Get closer, really quietly
6 Cartoon soldier
7 "American ___" (TV show)
8 Order from a mug shot photographer
9 "For shame!" noise
10 "The Aristocats" kitten, or his composer namesake Hector
11 Rental company with orange and white vans
12 Montana city
16 Monopoly card
18 Taekwondo great Jhoon ___
22 Sorrowful Portuguese folk music (anagram of OF AD)
23 Disco ___ ("The Simpsons" character)
25 Eugene of "American Reunion"
26 Fly with the eagles
27 Record for later
28 "Break ___!" (words to an actor)
31 Falls into a chair haphazardly
32 Play that introduced the term "robot"
33 Killer whale
34 Linguist Chomsky
35 In ___ (at heart)
37 Business execs in charge of the numbers
40 Welcome, like the new year
41 Tiger Woods's ex
42 German coin, before adopting the euro
43 Bug
45 Jason's ship, or a Best Picture winning movie
46 ___ Capital (company founded by Mitt Romney)
47 Extreme curve in a river
48 Actress Kate of "Dynasty"
49 High, low and ebb, at the beach
52 One of the Great Lakes
53 Poultry
54 Decked out (in)
55 Jesus's water-into-wine city
57 Slimy stuff
58 Place to see exotic animals

2

GQ

Across

1. Like some mattresses
5. Cat of many colors
11. Cranberry growing site
14. Section
15. ___ acid (anagram of ICETAC)
16. Prefix for -logist
17. Table salt, in chemistry class
18. Mountain where Noah landed his ark
19. Brazilian city, for short
20. Worked hard on a mathematical proof?
23. Mahatma Gandhi's country
25. Secret agent's activity
26. Leading figure on a long journey?
31. Really slow, on sheet music
32. ___ dish (not the main course)
33. Nobel Prize-winning novelist Gordimer
35. Roadside bomb letters
36. ___ vert (green bean, in French cuisine)
37. Opposite of on
40. For each one
44. Scotch and ___ (drink)
45. Create
47. Voyage to see the world's great bedcovers?
49. Yell at the top of your lungs
51. Bring up, as a child
52. Marketer's popularity quotient for Limburger?
57. Curvy letter
58. Whole
59. Person from Copenhagen
62. "My Big Fat Greek Wedding" star Vardalos
63. Elvis Costello hit, or singer Krauss
64. Radio host Don
65. Devour
66. Highest-quality
67. Between eight and ten

Down

1. It keeps you cool in summer
2. 401(k) alternative
3. Went out slowly
4. Sick-and-tired feeling
5. James who played Sonny Corleone
6. Farmland measurement
7. Heavy metal
8. Macy Gray's first hit song
9. Italian goodbyes
10. One of eight kids born at the same time
11. Trademarked swimsuit that covers everything except the face
12. Cuban region from the Spanish for "East"
13. Words uttered in disbelief
21. Mouse's cousin
22. Bread used for a reuben sandwich
23. Stanford-Binet test scores
24. Rapa ___ (Easter Island)
27. Make noise with two fingers
28. Former Iraqi Deputy Prime Minister Aziz (anagram of QI RAT)
29. French goodbye
30. Actress Christina of 2012's "Bel Ami"
34. "Mad Dogs and Englishmen" writer Coward
36. Quit standing
37. X-rated
38. Reddish-purple shade
39. Aims for
41. Substitute
42. Japanese paper-folding art
43. Slam
44. Monkey's cousin
46. Incredible Hulk co-creator Stan
48. Prefix meaning "three"
50. ___ Park (Thomas Edison's home)
53. Ear cleaner
54. Increase
55. Elvis's middle name
56. Mind
60. Sister in a convent
61. Ending for Japan or Taiwan

3

Meet the Beetles

Across

1 Clear alcoholic drinks
7 NCO rank: abbr.
10 Clenched hand
14 Too
15 Desserts with layers
17 ___ hearts (red playing card)
18 "Coming on stung all the time..."
19 "I'll climb on your kitchen countertop, if it makes you feel alright..."
21 Beaver Cleaver exclamations
22 One-named English singer
23 "Every Kiss Begins with..." jeweler
26 Group of schools in one area, for short (hidden in JAMES DEAN)
27 Center of a peach
29 Weasel that's white in the winter
31 Ray varieties
34 Woman's name
35 "The girl that's driving me mad is chirping away..."
39 ___-purpose (having two uses)
40 "My Fair Lady" lyricist (partner of Loewe)
41 Canada's capital
44 Snake that killed Cleopatra
45 The New York Knicks, Los Angeles Lakers, etc.
48 "Moonrise Kingdom" director Anderson
49 Unsettled feeling
52 Fuel source called "black diamonds"
53 "Ah, look at all the lonely pincers..."
56 "And you're burrowing for no one but me..."
59 Scottish dish that looks a bit unappetizing
60 Singles, doubles, triples and home runs
61 Golfer Els and comic Kovacs
62 Went down quickly
63 Enzyme suffix
64 Knox or Bynes

Down

1 Phone company with an orange logo
2 Sheep
3 Like cans sold cheap
4 Dobie Gillis' friend Maynard G. ___
5 Matty or Felipe of baseball
6 Network that brings you the movie "Piranhaconda"
7 Did cloak-and-dagger work
8 One of Aesop's tales
9 Cuisine with jambalaya
10 Notoriety
11 Three, in ancient Rome
12 Amtrak stop: abbr.
13 Mao ___-tung
16 Overheated condition
20 Hot Wheels toy company
23 Jason at point guard, or a famous pirate
24 "The Diary of ___ Frank"
25 Positive vote
27 ___-man (video game)
28 Fluid in a pen
30 Former Israeli PM Golda
31 Actress Kunis of "Black Swan"
32 "The dog ___ my homework"
33 Layers
35 Like kitten videos
36 What Charlie Brown says when he's mad
37 Run-___ (some sentences)
38 Sales agent
39 ___ Jones Industrial Average
42 "America's Most Wanted" host John
43 Blood issue
45 Brain, in slang
46 Treated way too nicely
47 Milano of "Who's the Boss?"
50 Tiny fliers
51 Taste, touch or sight
52 Competitor of Aetna and Humana
53 ___ out a living (scraped by)
54 Perlman of "Cheers"
55 Not quite hot
56 Channel that reairs "The Big Bang Theory"
57 Potent ending?
58 CBS franchise show

4

British Invasion

Across

1. "Unbelievable" band of 1991
4. Singer Dylan, or one of the Grimm Brothers
9. Take by mouth
13. Actor DiCaprio, to fans
14. Washington State city
15. Stupor
16. Writing assignment that, through complete luck, got an A?
18. Greek vowels that look like an H
19. Did away with Homer's neighbor for good?
21. Rapper who sounds like he's a physician
23. ___ out a living
24. Item rolled in a casino
25. Axton of "Gremlins"
26. Exhale like a dog
29. Female
31. ___-Tzu (Chinese philosopher)
32. Song played on a sitar
33. The ___ Four (Beatles)
34. Band of John Wayne-loving computer programmers?
39. Have debts
40. It's good to hear after a spill
41. Shady tree
43. Leg bone
46. ___-rock (music genre)
47. Popeye's kid ___'Pea
48. That, in Spanish
49. "Call Me Maybe" singer Carly ___ Jepsen
51. Early ___ (no night owl)
52. Completely fooled one of the Beverly Hillbillies?
57. Blue: Sp.
58. Bumper sticker slogan for Stooges fans?
61. ___ and void
62. Fixed sock holes
63. 56, in old Rome
64. "___ does that star-spangled banner..."
65. ___-Hawley Tariff
66. Have some food

Down

1. Little creature who helps Santa
2. "Spaceballs" director Brooks
3. Seeker's cry to the hider
4. Mock (hidden in NINJA PEST)
5. Mil. school
6. Head: Ger.
7. Brunch dish
8. Former Israeli prime minister
9. Took way too much
10. Warning on video games with lots of gore
11. Hank who voices Chief Wiggum
12. Take down a notch
14. Precocious kid
17. MTV mainstay Loder
20. New Jersey city
21. Rival of UPS and FedEx
22. Street
26. Rate of speed
27. In the past
28. Lowest point
30. ___-Wan Kenobi
32. Money for finding a lost pet
33. Toad's cousin
35. Pond fish
36. Punk offshoot (hidden in DEMOTED)
37. Fresh way of doing things
38. Popular TV show with lots of music
42. Debussy's "La ___"
43. Selena's music genre
44. Rodeos and Troopers, e.g.
45. Actor Scott of "Quantum Leap"
46. Train in a 1974 movie title, or its 2009 remake
47. ___ Spin (classic toy)
50. Heartburn causes, maybe
51. No longer working: abbr.
53. Pocoyo's pachyderm friend
54. Prefix before space
55. Fighting word that means "hand"
56. ___-à-porter
59. College founded by Thomas Jefferson
60. ___ Kat (candy bar)

5   The Big Build-Up

Across

1 Old theater name
7 Actor Oka of "Heroes" (anagram of SIAM)
11 Good nickname for a plumber?
14 Like some non-permanent art exhibits
15 "By the look ___..."
16 Line of seats, as in a theater
17 Write down "Vast Asian country with a population of over a billion"?
19 One billion years
20 Notable time periods
21 Paddle's cousin
22 Creatures from outer space
24 Fifth qtrs.
25 Newt (hidden in LEFTY)
26 What an angry bee can do
27 Crazy situation in "The King's Speech"?
31 ___ corpus
34 Small battery size
35 Bullets
36 On guard
37 Every little bit
38 Fashion designer Calvin ___
39 ___-Flush (former bathroom cleaner brand)
40 Poli ___ (college field of study)
41 They produce mushroom clouds
42 Steal a parachute pants-wearing rapper's plane?
45 Kate's sitcom partner, in the 1980s
46 Guy's counterpart
47 "___ du lieber!"
50 Malfunctions, like a printer
52 Endodontist's degree: abbr.
53 Razor line introduced by Gillette
54 Inventor Whitney
55 Leader of the course "Denial 101"?
58 Actor Cheadle
59 Heidi of "Project Runway"
60 Ultimate
61 "___ My Party"
62 Himalayan giant
63 Slender

Down

1 Event with cowboys and clowns
2 Like xenon, as gases go
3 Some Italian cars, for short
4 ___ Lane (Clark Kent co-worker)
5 Light brown shade
6 On our side
7 "SNL" alum Jay
8 Org. with a "100 Years..." series
9 Frank of the Rat Pack
10 Slanted type of type
11 Apps that cost nothing, say
12 Crazy as a ___
13 Possesses
18 "E! News" co-host Sadler (sounds like an animal)
23 Asthmatic's item
25 Coup d'___
26 ___ of approval
27 TV dramas, generally
28 Sofia Coppola's aunt ___ Shire
29 Leave out
30 Not daughters
31 ___ browns (breakfast food)
32 Jai ___ (ball sport)
33 Franklin, Carson and Moore
37 Pain
38 "Hooked on Classics" record label (hidden in BLACK TELEPHONE)
40 One of two held by a mountain athlete
41 Best Picture winner about Mozart
43 Really inelegant
44 People who run a store: abbr.
47 Playwright Fugard (hidden in CATHOLIC)
48 Toothpaste brand
49 "The Outcasts of Poker Flat" writer Bret
50 "Return of the ___"
51 Oodles
52 Moore of "G.I. Jane"
53 Wile E. Coyote's supplier
56 Place
57 Off-roader

Tally Ho!

Across

1 ___ worker (non-permanent staff)
5 1/100th division: abbr.
8 Start of a song's refrain
13 Quarterback Tony
14 "Oops..."
15 Deadly snake
16 He had the 1994 #1 hit "Here Comes the Hotstepper"
18 Key that's the same as B
19 Gusto
20 People who sell cars
22 Capital of Ghana
25 Literary character who had a title "Prayer for" him
27 Totally sad
29 Away from the wind
30 Prefix meaning "times one trillion" (anagram of RATE)
31 Poisonous fish
33 Sought out quickly
38 Emma Watson role in the Harry Potter movies
41 German city on the Ruhr (hidden in MESSENGER)
42 Filled with wonder
43 Lady ___ (pop singer)
44 Havana's island
46 ___ number (product identifier)
48 He played the bossy Stooge
53 Second largest city in France
54 Triangular houses
55 Thing
57 Hiccup, for instance
58 It may be involved in tallying the four theme answers
63 Yaphet of "Alien" and "The Running Man"
64 Messes up
65 French cheese
66 Pal of the knife and fork
67 86,400 seconds
68 Shut the door hard

Down

1 Prefix meaning "three"
2 One billion years
3 2001, in Roman numerals
4 Where you might have a pair of jacks or a straight flush
5 Opening for graph
6 Due to, in slang
7 It comes "after me," in a Louis XV quote
8 What news anchors face
9 Winchester gun
10 Cop ___
11 Hear (about)
12 More suitable for a film festival than the local multiplex, say
14 Thurman of "Bel Ami"
17 Jai ___
21 Dir. opposite WSW
22 Foaming ___ mouth
23 Native Canadians
24 Caleb and John Dickson, for two
26 Be belligerent
28 Accounts head, for short
32 Without apologizing
34 They run with torches
35 New Zealand mystery writer Marsh (anagram of O GAIN)
36 Indie band ___ and Sara (anagram of AGENT)
37 Heard tests
39 Shared, like a characteristic
40 Map lines: abbr.
45 Much-maligned director Boll (hidden in YOU WENT)
47 Basic util.
48 Costume party covers
49 King ___ (Michael Jackson title)
50 Muse of love poetry
51 Lacks other options
52 Journal
56 End zone scores, for short
59 Major time period
60 Website address
61 "My Big Fat Greek Wedding" star Vardalos
62 President pro ___

7

What's That Sound?

Across

1. "The Princess and the ___"
4. "SNL" alum Horatio
8. Exploded
14. Patent holder, often: abbr.
15. Song from Sarah McLachlan's "Surfacing" (hidden in RADIATOR)
16. Actor Tom, or a kind of vacation
17. Gun gp.
18. HINT FOR SOUNDALIKE #1
20. Facts
22. Former Miami Heat star, familiarly
23. 1966 Michael Caine role
24. Visibly shocked
26. Tony-winning one-man play of 1989 (hidden in INTRUDE)
27. 502, in Roman numerals
28. Go back to the book
30. "Can ___ least sit down?"
32. Gps. like CARE and Amnesty International, to the UN
35. HINT FOR SOUNDALIKE #2
38. Where, in Latin
41. End of university web sites
42. Once around the track
43. Pull a waterskier
44. HINT FOR SOUNDALIKE #3
48. Lemony Snicket villain
49. Reno and Holder, for short
50. OK to eat
54. Gunky stuff
56. "This ___ test..."
58. ___ Wrap (plastic wrap brand)
59. Bronze medalist's place
61. Amt. on a food package
63. Talk show host with a "Jaywalking" segment
64. HINT FOR SOUNDALIKE #4
67. Soccer's Freddy (hidden in HEAD UP)
68. Spanish chant
69. Cab
70. Get droopy
71. Steal cattle
72. Doctors who check out head colds, for short
73. With 1-across, phonetic representation of the four soundalikes

Down

1. Odist with a type of ode named for him
2. Make royally angry
3. James Cameron movie that outgrossed his own "Titanic"
4. Gullible guy
5. Fusses
6. Not, in German
7. CNN host Fareed
8. 1/100th div.
9. "Whether good ___..."
10. Doing some knitting, maybe
11. Many a Three Stooges melee
12. Morales of "La Bamba"
13. 2000s Bengals running back Dorsey
19. With even distribution
21. On the ocean
25. Group of experts
29. "___ ever wonder..."
31. Swap
33. Ear-related prefix
34. U-turn from NNE
36. Posing, as for the camera
37. Some Apple computers
38. Flying saucer
39. ___ Harbour, Fla.
40. Dreams up
45. "Can't quite recall..."
46. Washington, West Virginia or Wyoming
47. Soap brand
51. Chicken piece
52. Martin who played Bela Lugosi in "Ed Wood"
53. Plenty
55. Former "Access Hollywood" host Nancy
57. Phrase for the slightly miffed and disappointed
59. Norse god
60. Website to watch old shows
62. Send a quick message to
65. Riddle-me-___ (old kids' rhyme)
66. Bro's sibling

Hybrid Cars

Across

1 McMuffin ingredients
5 Canterbury religious title
15 Bunches
16 Little shaver
17 Hybrid pickup with really low visibility?
19 Bowling achievement
20 Torah repositories
21 Seabird that can be "sooty"
22 D.C. United's org.
24 Minuscule, in slang
25 ISP that used to mail free trial discs
28 It may feature a store from a mile away
33 Hybrid car that floats in the ocean?
39 Morales of "NYPD Blue" and "La Bamba"
40 New York city on the Mohawk River
41 Depend (on)
42 Hybrid car with a really old sound system?
45 Very fast animal
46 Pallid
47 Comedian Kennedy
51 She was Dorothy on "The Golden Girls"
53 "I ___ top of the world!"
54 Snare
58 Academy Award
62 Hybrid car that runs a few seconds, then stops, then runs again, then stops again...?
65 Get past the highs and lows
66 "Right Now (Na Na Na)" rapper (anagram of AN OK)
67 Classification for comfortable jeans or shirts
68 Salt's performing partner, in a 1980s hip-hop group

Down

1 Consumes
2 Unidentifiable stuff on a cafeteria tray
3 "Saturn Devouring His Son" painter
4 Nasty weather
5 Legendary Notre Dame coach Parseghian
6 ___-tat-tat
7 Russian ruler, once
8 Sell to a pawn shop
9 Super Mario ___
10 Computer company
11 Blue-gray shade, or an online magazine
12 Tony-winning actress Uta ___
13 Unpleasant scents
14 Flower once a national emblem of China
18 "Kojak" actor Savalas
23 "I miss you ___!"
24 College URL ender
25 Banda ___ (Indonesian city; anagram of EACH)
26 Pretentious phrase of emphasis
27 Slender
29 Folk rocker ___ Curtis (anagram of ACE IT)
30 Not dead
31 Permissible
32 1981 Genesis album that's also a rhyme scheme
34 Kid-___ (G-rated movies)
35 Hockey legend Bobby
36 Yelp of sudden pain
37 Jazz legend Fitzgerald
38 Actress Cannon
43 High card
44 FOX series
47 Bad guy in "Aladdin"
48 Make ___ (go, in chess)
49 Spongy-looking mushroom variety
50 Hindu god of war (anagram of DRAIN)
52 Musician's rights gp.
54 Buster Brown's dog
55 Marsh growth
56 Since
57 Watermelon seed spitting noise
59 Birthday food
60 Perched upon
61 "Mazes and Monsters" novelist Jaffe
63 Send a document
64 Letters in telecom

9

Thank You

Across

1 They're older than jrs.
4 "Trial of the Century" figure Kaelin
8 Place for a manicure
11 X-rated
13 Frozen cause of water blockage
16 Not dry
17 Suit to ___
18 Do what a quarterback does
20 Sense of house-selling skills nearby?
22 Movie catalog listings
23 Country singer Twain
24 Little laugh
25 "She had ___ Presbyterian mind..."--Steinbeck
27 Well past mourning a broken egg?
31 Apiece
32 "___ All Ye Faithful"
33 "Are you a man ___ mouse?"
36 Spans over lovely rivers?
41 Odysseus's faithful dog in "The Odyssey" (anagram of SO RAG)
42 "___ Groove" (1985 hip-hop movie)
43 Take quickly (away from)
46 Like some stews
47 Claim from a video store stocking "Bulworth" and "Reds"?
51 Pasta sold in a bag
52 Third-century year
54 Agnus ___
55 Vipers and boa constrictors
56 Many-___ (multicolored)
57 Christmas ___ (Dec. 24th)
58 Days gone by
59 Where cops work: abbr.

Down

1 Patty Hearst's captors
2 Bring back
3 Stevia, alternatively
4 St. ___ and Nevis
5 Needing some rubbing
6 University of Maryland athlete, for short
7 Skunk's scent
8 NFL Hall-of-Famer Lynn
9 Oscar winner Joe of "Goodfellas"
10 In a daze
12 Person giving the cards out, at a poker table
14 More great
15 Prepare potatoes
19 Rush drummer Neil (anagram of TAPER)
21 Internet writing system that popularized "pwn'd" (hidden in SLEETING)
22 Type of roof for a muscle car
25 Sailor's greetings
26 Asinine
28 Mifflin's publishing partner
29 Prefix with -plasm
30 Sack lunch item that needs a spoon
34 Did a hairdo differently
35 Pale
37 Use, as a dining room table
38 Ursus ___ (scientific name for the brown bear; anagram of CROATS)
39 Furniture chain
40 Rachel who played Debbie Downer on "SNL"
43 Stockholm resident
44 Israeli desert
45 Texas A&M student
46 "Steppenwolf" author Hermann
48 Historic event when 43-downs switched to driving on the right (anagram of Y HAD)
49 Nevada county
50 Pabst or Heineken
53 Driver's licenses, e.g.

14

10

That Show Is So Corny

Across

1 Part of a movie
6 Fridge stickers
13 1992 Madonna album
15 Arctic herd member
16 Corny game show set on city streets?
17 Carbon-14, for one
18 East, in Germany (hidden in HOSTED)
19 Drag (around)
21 Extremely cold (hidden in HUGE LIDS)
22 Corny reality show set all over the world, with "The"?
27 Legendary king of Crete
29 Deschanel of "New Girl"
30 More slippery and gooey
32 ___-cone
33 Typical guy on romance novel covers
37 With 39-across, corny buddy cop show?
39 See 37-across
41 ___ problem with (doesn't like)
42 Get some grub
44 Party
45 Magazine that popularized the term "crowdsourcing"
47 Name of three Shakespearean title kings
48 Corny coming-of-age dramedy?
53 Label for Arab meat dealers
54 Obedience school lesson
55 Koppel or Williams
58 Home perm brand
61 And all these corny TV shows are brought to you by the dating site...
64 Plants the grass after it dries out, say
65 Slowly slide into chaos
66 The O in Jackie O
67 "Cagney & ___"

Down

1 Mrs.'s counterparts, in Mexico
2 Family on "Seinfeld"
3 Biblical verb ending
4 CNN's ___ Robertson (hidden in PANICKY)
5 2011 outbreak cause
6 Sprint competitor, once
7 Some batteries
8 Just barely awake and functioning
9 Fertilizer component
10 Virus named for a Congolese river
11 Subject of debate
12 Rain-unfriendly material
13 Earth Day prefix
14 Rife with conversation
20 Cheap cars of the 1990s
23 "Chaplin" actress Kelly
24 "Hey, wait ___!"
25 New Rochelle, N.Y. college
26 Some Chryslers
27 ___ pit
28 Letter after theta
31 Major German river, in German
33 More bashful
34 Subway barrier
35 Rehab participant
36 It's between S and F on a laptop
38 36 inches
40 Qatar's capital (anagram of HAD O)
43 Concert concession stand buys
45 Howling beasts
46 Cut and ___ (clear)
48 Top-to-bottom, informally
49 Actress Uta ___
50 Actress Donovan of "Clueless"
51 Part of the United Kingdom
52 Lucy's friend, on "I Love Lucy"
56 One of the deadly sins
57 Color Easter Eggs
59 Former dictator ___ Amin
60 Curvy letter
62 Eggs, to a biologist
63 Leather shoe, for short

Outside Protection

Across

1 English homework list, for short
6 Health gp. based in Atlanta
9 Like stray dogs
14 Coral island
15 Bird that's a pet for Harry Potter
16 "The Path to the Nest of Spiders" writer Calvino (hidden in VITAL ORGANS)
17 Comedian Anderson
18 Crunchy stuff in a walkway
20 Final Four gp.
22 A, in Austria
23 Late-night host Jay
24 He released the album "So"
28 FBI worker, for short
29 Yang's counterpart
30 Pre-album collectibles
31 Faux ___
34 High school dance, for short
36 Genetic messenger material
38 From the beginning, in Latin
40 Trucker's less-green alternative to biofuel
44 Skipped the restaurant
45 "A curse on your family!"
46 Being, to Berlioz
47 987-65-4321, e.g.
48 102, in Roman numerals
51 Sneaky
53 "___ was going to say before you interrupted me..."
54 What a mom might picture a secretly-bratty kid to be
57 Largest of the continents
60 Tic-tac-toe line
61 Girlfriend, in France
62 Staff
65 "Sex, Lies and Videotape" actress MacDowell
68 Poet Sylvia
69 ___ Soundsystem
70 Dog
71 Electronics name
72 Designer monogram under the Gucci label
73 "Find ___ and fill it"

Down

1 Actor Kilmer
2 Prefix meaning "ear-related"
3 Advice to the angry
4 She "Doesn't Live Here Anymore"
5 Like the eyes of the sleep-deprived
6 Policeman
7 Dorky type
8 "Marie ___" (fashion mag)
9 Defunct space station
10 In any way
11 Church passage
12 "By the Time I Get to Phoenix" singer Campbell
13 2012 acronym akin to "Be adventurous"
19 ___ Gnop (retro game of the 1970s)
21 "It's ___!" (maternity ward shout)
24 Season 4 "Bachelorette" DeAnna
25 Long-plumed herons
26 Novelist Tyler
27 Actor Morales of "NYPD Blue"
31 Stamp when there aren't enough stamps
32 Reluctant (to)
33 Cirque du ___
35 Hosp. scanner
37 "___ Wiedersehen!"
39 Spelling ___
41 "___ upon a time..."
42 "Random" abbr. on a moving box
43 Greek letter that's also an airline
49 Heavy metal
50 "Wouldn't that be awesome..."
52 Kawasaki competitor
54 Pale looking
55 Business decision-makers
56 Sheer, smooth fabric
57 iPhone buys
58 Actress Ward
59 Iraq neighbor
63 "And what have we here!?!"
64 The "bad" cholesterol, for short
66 Dvorak's Symphony No. 9 ___ Minor
67 Announcer Hall

Two-Card Stud

Across

1 Words before "friends" or "careful out there"

7 "___ Carter" (Lil Wayne album series) (anagram of HAT)

10 "Don't let your boss catch you watching this" acronym

14 Common baseball situation

15 Hua ___ (Thai beach resort; hidden in THINKING)

16 Glow

17 Categorize

18 Summer hrs. in South Carolina

19 Air quality problem

20 A pair of cards reduced to a fine powder?

23 Six, to Italians

24 Make ___ of (write down)

25 Sphere in a scepter

28 A pair of cards, a few hours from now?

33 Tic-tac-toe line

34 General ___'s chicken (Chinese restaurant dish)

35 Actress Turner

36 GI's stint peeling potatoes, for example

39 Put in the slammer

41 Singer Clapton

42 ___ in "Oscar"

45 Wall St. worker (hidden in CARBON)

46 Pair of cards with unreasonable aspirations?

51 Actress Lucy of "Elementary"

52 Singer Guthrie and street skater Eisenberg

53 "Weetzie Bat" author Francesca ___ Block

55 Pair of cards that are...a pair of cards?

60 Actress Tara

62 "My Big Fat Greek Wedding" star Vardalos

63 Like people from Mogadishu

64 Start the poker pot

65 "Srsly?!?!"

66 Words to a ship's captain

67 "Naked Maja" painter

68 Peg used in golf

69 Malaria-carrying fly

Down

1 A bunch

2 Follows

3 Boston Red Sox song covered by the Dropkick Murphys

4 Chimney sweep's grime

5 ___ Khalifa (world's tallest building)

6 "I'd Rather Go Blind" singer ___ James

7 Popular wedding website, or what's tied at a wedding

8 Grotesque

9 Like some security software

10 Poet Ogden ___

11 Redundant count

12 1970s 'do

13 Move like a happy hound's tail

21 Half-___ (coffee mix)

22 Toothpaste variety

26 Actress Russo

27 Singer Paisley

29 Certify, with "for"

30 Abbr. on a business card

31 Reply to a liar

32 Excuse

36 Hip spelling of "cool"

37 Toyota hybrids, jokingly

38 Lack of cohesiveness

40 Noah's boat

43 Greatest of ___

44 Room for carry-ons

47 Groupie

48 That, in Tijuana

49 Div. including the Braves and Phillies

50 Old sitcom character Dobie ___

54 Engulfed in flames

56 Thought

57 "The City ___ War" (Cobra Starship song)

58 Playthings

59 Captain Hook's mate

60 Cleaning cloth

61 "Achtung Baby" co-producer Brian

Themelessly Yours

Across

1 Muddy spectator "sport"
12 Mauna ___, Hawaii
15 Reality TV kid who drinks Go-Go Juice and showed her belly to the judges
16 Furthermore
17 Tudor symbol
18 General who's an enemy of Superman (hidden in JAZZ ODDS)
19 Keep a ship from leaving port, maybe
20 On the line
22 Headwear banned by the NFL
24 Words that can precede a proverb
25 Robert who played A.J. Soprano
27 Word in wedding notices
28 Big name in skydiving?
32 Brown eraser variety
36 Banned apple spray
37 Had a yearning
39 Unit of loudness
40 JPEG alternative
42 Kind of prison, for short
44 ___ of a kind
45 Give off, like charm
46 Actress Nicollette
50 Romanian composer George of the opera "Oedipe"
55 Betty Crocker product
56 Hall and ___
57 Folk rocker DiFranco
58 Computer chip slogan
62 Director Howard or former congressman Paul
63 Shop owner
64 ___ newton (cookie)
65 Payment alternative to checks

Down

1 Freudian concept
2 They brought you the Popeil Pocket Fisherman
3 Wrath
4 Late "Queen of Salsa" ___ Cruz
5 Making a segue (to)
6 Docs for women only
7 "Ruh-___!" (Scooby-Doo phrase)
8 "___ favor" (Spanish for "please")
9 German WWII craft
10 Utterly befuddled
11 "Guys and Dolls" composer/lyricist Frank
12 Former file-sharing site
13 Mushroom used in Japanese cooking
14 Threw in
21 African fly
23 Put on, like comfier clothes
24 Affixes T-shirt designs
26 Pink Floyd label
28 Chatter
29 Pharmaceutical company ___ Lilly
30 Mouse's relative
31 At least
33 Democrats' rivals, for short
34 A, in French
35 Dudes
38 Eisenhower's command, for short (hidden in RETOLD)
41 Belief in hidden spiritual creatures
43 Woodworker, when doing some joining
46 Cold-weather wear
47 Vietnam's capital
48 ___ out (managing)
49 Musician Hoyt ___ (who also appeared in "Gremlins")
51 Alleviated
52 Michael of R.E.M.
53 One who gives up
54 Site visitors
59 Before
60 "Law," in Spanish
61 When doubled, a 1965 Dixie Cups song

Fore and Aff

Across

1 1972 Bill Withers hit
6 "Hair" co-author James
10 "The Naked ___" (Goya painting)
14 Their fight song says "There goes old Georgetown"
15 Dedicated poems
16 Fits of anger
17 Fancy sleeve adornment
19 "___ not good, I'll call you back"
20 In an aerodynamic way
21 Home of a Herculean lion (hidden in BONE MEASUREMENT)
22 "I ___ the fool who..."
24 Tennis court divider
25 President Ford
26 Like factory second clothing: abbr.
27 Table scrap (hidden in PORTABLE)
28 Elevated flat top, or an Arizona city
29 When doubled, a Teletubby
30 Financial coinage in 2012 headlines
35 Grammy-winner Baker
37 Make eggs
38 Ed of "The Mary Tyler Moore Show"
39 Ate the rest of
42 Forbes 400 member, often
43 How you feel
44 Inc., in Paris (hidden in RACIER)
45 "Deep Space Nine" shapeshifter (hidden in GOOD ONE)
46 Humanoid creature
49 Sandwich known by three letters
50 "Hey, over here!"
51 Organ that pumps blood
52 Send the family newsletter, say
54 Prefix meaning "within"
55 "And don't try any ___!"
58 Query to Brutus
59 "___ Love Her"
60 Dance done with a stick
61 Picks up the tab
62 Pear variety
63 ___ a million

Down

1 "Weird Al" Yankovic movie
2 Fraternity's female counterpart: abbr.
3 Problem when you read too much
4 Macho
5 Ending for coal or opal
6 Device used in speed tests
7 Grownup
8 Go against
9 Annual Ashland event, for short (hidden in GOSFORD)
10 Vitamins and ___
11 Scent
12 Amethyst or turquoise
13 Longtime Syrian president
18 Painter Matisse
21 Brand near the Sanka
22 Rice dish
23 Like someone from Tehran
25 Shaving cream alternative
27 Categorized similarly
28 Minnesota medical group
31 Heel
32 All dressed up for Halloween
33 Gives grub to
34 ___ Loops (cereal)
36 Fearful
40 Pig
41 How marathon runners walk around
46 Baby bird sound
47 Gossipmonger
48 Totally bonkers
49 Music groups
50 Vladimir of Russia
52 Monocular character on "Yo Gabba Gabba!" (anagram of UM, NO)
53 Capital of Norway
55 Awesome
56 J. Edgar Hoover ran it
57 Sprint calling card from the 1980s (hidden in THE FONZ)

It's a Scream!

Across

1 Built to ___
5 President/playwright Havel
11 Breakfast burrito ingredient
14 Frosty the Snowman's eyes
15 Lizard some keep as a pet
16 Ruin
17 Dancer Ailey, in his upstate New York home (as screamed on "Chipmunk Day Afternoon")?
19 Arafat's gp., once
20 Macbeth's title
21 Flower part
22 Peace signs
23 "The Jungle Book" boy
25 Squirrel's stash
27 Rueful word
28 Number of Belgian beers you plan on drinking (as screamed in "A Futbol Named Desire")?
32 Napoleonic marshal (hidden in HONEYED)
33 "Hey there, cowboy!"
34 Like Donald Trump's lips, often
35 "Yeah, whatever..."
37 War horse
40 Heart chambers
41 "The Conning Tower" writer and Algonquin Round Table member, for short (hidden in WOLFPACK)
44 Genghis's 100%-wooden cousin (as screamed in "Lumberjack Trek II")?
46 Former Swedish automaker
47 Relaxation
48 Like scratchy throats
50 It gets wrinkles out of clothes
51 Bed, in Spanish
55 TV's Huxtable and Kojak, for two
56 Dir. opposite SSE
57 Time leading up to doing whatever you want (as screamed on "Golf Course Braveheart")?
59 "Isn't that somethin'?"
60 ___ del Fuego
61 "Morning Joe" co-host Brzezinski
62 Leb. neighbor
63 Winter Olympics ski course
64 List-ending abbr.

Down

1 Actor Crothers
2 Road danger
3 Erode
4 Holds tightly (to)
5 By way of
6 "Jumpin' Jack Flash, it's ___..."
7 Religious offshoot
8 Cleanse (anagram of VEAL)
9 Cat or kangaroo
10 Mover's vehicle
11 Ruler like Caesar
12 Lead ore samples (anagram of ANGELA'S)
13 How some things are overstated
18 Animation collectible
22 Dance popularized by Madonna in the 1990s
24 Avoided serious injury
26 "It's a Wonderful Life" director Frank
29 Make some changes
30 Archie Bunker's wife
31 Unitard material
33 Goes out of sight
35 "Rio" singer Simon
36 "___ that the truth"
37 Orchestra section
38 "ER" actress Maura
39 Give more control to
41 Tricked everyone
42 Average klutz
43 Lower than low
45 Firing after-effect
46 Big plan
49 Suffix with Manhattan
52 Geometry calculation
53 Crossword great ___ Reagle (hidden in SUMMER LOVE)
54 Big do
57 Dix and Ticonderoga, e.g.
58 Aries animal

Four Legs Good

Across

1 There's one at the beginning of each of this puzzle's four theme entries
7 Retail estab.
10 Holder and RFK, for short
13 "Nets to Catch the Wind" poet Wylie
14 "King ___" (Shakespeare play)
15 Sign for a packed theater
16 Getting gray
17 Ways out
19 Sketch show with Dollar Bill Montgomery
20 Bart Simpson word
21 Landers of advice
23 1 of 18 on a golf course
24 Explorer with a Colorado peak named after him
29 2500, in Roman numerals
32 Chef Lagasse who says "Pork fat rules!"
33 Had some ham, say
34 Type of 1-across, in Mexico
35 Burn in the tub
36 Day between Mon. and Wed.
37 Leader of 1960s UK rockers The Pacemakers
38 Perfect scores, often
39 ___ Harbour, Fla.
40 Shown past the foyer
41 "What is it?"
42 Native American group (and source of a Washington city that differs by one letter)
44 Yell on a golf course
45 Pop-up blockers block them
46 Pain-blocking drug
50 Like growly stomachs
55 Comfortable seat
56 Harlem theater named for a Greek god
57 Mai ___ (cocktail)
58 "It's either him ___!"
59 "I thought it'd never get here!"
60 Damascus's country: abbr.
61 Lofty poem
62 Notable feature of each 1-across

Down

1 Grin from ear to ear
2 Korbut of gymnastics
3 Competed
4 "What's ___ for me?"
5 Illegitimate
6 Unit of work
7 She played drums on "Seven Nation Army"
8 Singing in a bar
9 Stereo knob
10 Org.
11 Oldest boy on "The Brady Bunch"
12 Baseball great Sammy
14 Zodiac sign
18 Take to court
20 MSNBC rival
22 Lon ___ (palindromic coup leader)
24 Spicy
25 Pageant host
26 Lima and pinto
27 Addresses that may be stored in "Favorites"
28 Comic Poundstone
29 Nixon whose voice replaced Natalie Wood's in "West Side Story" (anagram of RAM IN)
30 Golden Arches sandwich
31 "Love Will Lead You Back" singer Taylor
34 Turn
36 Don't rush
37 Reaches, as a high point
39 One of the Seven Sisters colleges
40 Lamentable
42 Chocolate drink once pitched by Yogi Berra
43 Guy
44 Govt. arm that oversees TV
46 Food in a horse's feedbag
47 Internal scan
48 Giant slain by Odin, thus creating the Earth (anagram of RIMY)
49 Intense anger
51 ___ contendere (court plea)
52 Flavor ___ (rapper)
53 Besides
54 Connect the ___
56 Ooh and ___

Rated R (for Relocation)

Across

1 Mensa members' stats
4 Chic city near L.A.
10 Be civilly disobedient
14 Glass
15 In ___ (all together)
16 State whose capital is Des Moines
17 Tunnel effect created by blowing air through a line of empty-headed participants?
19 Gave prompts to
20 Former U.K. prime minister Tony
21 Supreme Court clothing
23 Idi with an evil history
24 Rival of NBC and ABC
27 Gaucho's rope
30 Channel that reruns "Family Feud"
31 Solo's attempt at an orchard?
34 Artificial, like body parts
35 One who's doomed
36 "Get outta here!"
39 Ltd., in the States
40 Civil War side against the Confederacy
41 Moon stage
42 Oil from orange blossoms (anagram of LOINER)
44 Guy who complains there are too many trees in the woods?
46 Guitarist Scaggs
49 ___ New Guinea
50 Part of a line: abbr.
51 U2 lead singer
52 Grand Ole ___
54 Like days of yore
55 Singer Mitchell
58 Idiot who drove his car into two feet of mud?
62 Yoked beasts
63 Sneaker brand
64 Actor Hakeem ___-Kazim of "24" (hidden in POLKAED)
65 No, to Nijinsky
66 Woke up after passing out
67 Slip up

Down

1 3-down remedy
2 Feelings that something's not right
3 Injury helped by a 1-down
4 Sierra Club founder John
5 Raggedy ___ (doll)
6 Tupperware top
7 Tel Aviv's country: abbr.
8 Rude person
9 Like many a Father's Day gift tie
10 Food associated with cable cars
11 Letters for debtors
12 Come up short on money
13 Little bit
18 Take first place
22 7-Eleven drink
24 Comedian Margaret
25 Annette of "Bugsy"
26 Black eyes
28 "Beloved" author Morrison
29 Chevy model
31 Comment after the bell
32 Rack up
33 Ending for north or south
34 Type of pricing
36 Letters on a sunscreen bottle
37 Karate move
38 ___ avis
43 TLA texted by teens
45 Landing spot for a plane
46 He rode in the General Lee
47 Like some garages, size-wise
48 "Doonesbury" character (anagram of KERZON)
51 Diner sandwich, for short
53 Little green man of the "Star Wars" movie
54 ___ buco (Italian dish)
55 "The Daily Show" host Stewart
56 Acne-fighting brand
57 French word in wedding notices
59 Crater's edge
60 Honorific poem
61 DC baseball player, for short

Secret Crossword

Across

1 Leap
5 Prefix meaning "both"
9 ___ moss
13 British children's author ___ Blyton
14 Actress Witherspoon
16 Baby ___ (candy bar)
17 UFO tracker's headwear, it's said
19 Writer Sarah ___ Jewett (hidden in SCORNED)
20 Be
21 Shrimp and salmon, it's said
23 Pollution-fighting org.
25 300, to Caesar
26 It figures heavily in the Mediterranean Diet, for short
27 Person from an Arabian Peninsula nation
31 Cake cover
33 They're full of old growth
38 Advertising award
39 "Heroes" villain (anagram of L-RAYS)
40 Out-of-control situation
43 Song title followed by "in all the wrong places"
46 Battery terminal
48 Walt ___
49 Bro or sis
50 Dog seen during "Family Ties" closing credits
53 Massive Brit. lexicon
54 Shar-pei's features
57 Bunch
62 Greek letter, or a tiny bit
63 Secret the theme answers contain
65 "Rhinestone Cowboy" singer Campbell
66 More weak, like excuses
67 Get off ___-free
68 Government org. "launched" in 1958
69 "Climb ___ Mountain" (song from "The Sound of Music")
70 Dick Tracy's love ___ Trueheart

Down

1 Ballet leap
2 Operating system option
3 Small
4 Some printable files
5 "All Things Considered" reporter Shapiro
6 Thin toast
7 Competitor of Glidden and Sherwin-Williams
8 Newton who discovered gravity
9 Univ. worker
10 Song contest with previous winners ABBA and Celine Dion
11 When many take lunch
12 Homework eater, supposedly
15 Suffix after "diet" or "synth"
18 "SNL" alum Cheri
22 Mark Harmon series on CBS
24 Belarus city not far from the similarly-named capital (anagram of PINKS)
27 TV channel for shoppers
28 Feel sick
29 Fossilized marine animals
30 "Have ___ time!"
32 "Save" shortcut on some computers
34 "I thought this'd be helpful" acronym
35 Former name of the cable network Versus (hidden in COOLNESS)
36 UK flying corps
37 Etch away
41 The ___ Glove ("As Seen on TV" mitt)
42 Scottish novelist Josephine
44 Egg, on a French menu
45 Fingerprint line
46 Pass out homework
47 Inventor Tesla
51 Prepare water for pasta
52 Arm bones
53 Willow variety
55 Grandma, to some
56 Forthcoming psych book
58 Robbie who played Cousin Oliver on "The Brady Bunch" (anagram of STIR)
59 Just a single time
60 Spacecrafts from another planet
61 ___ and pans
64 Not wet

19

Plant a Tree

Across

1. Winner
6. 50%
10. ___ the cows come home
13. "Raw" Crayola hue
14. ___ Lama
15. Vince's agent, on "Entourage"
16. Painter best known for being tall and stringy?
18. Penn of the "Harold & Kumar" franchise
19. Nutty ___ fruitcake
20. Nevada city, casually
21. Animal known for its laugh
23. Scribble (down)
24. Like hipster humor
25. Surf that's in charge of grilling the turf?
31. Not just once
32. Old saying
33. Actress Farrow
36. Pig's sound
37. Food Network celeb ___ de Laurentiis
38. Sage, for one
39. Lb. and mg, e.g.
40. New ___ (capital of India)
41. Classical architecture style
42. Really wants to get the stain out of a ticket?
44. Long-running Broadway musical, to fans
47. Wrath
48. Slack-jawed
49. Jai alai basket (anagram of CATES)
52. Roswell visitors
55. Greek goddess of night
56. Fast food chain run by Germany's Kohl?
59. Monkey's cousin
60. Last-minute greeting
61. Jazz singer Cleo
62. "___ just what I've always wanted!"
63. ___ mater (brain part; anagram of RAUD)
64. Family member, after tying the knot

Down

1. Castro's island
2. Managed care gps.
3. "Voulez-Vous" band from Sweden
4. Sea, to Debussy
5. Aggravate
6. Tennis star Mandlikova
7. Some beers
8. ___ Cruces, NM
9. Caviar, e.g.
10. Snatched
11. Tehran resident
12. Purple shade that's also a flower
14. Use a shovel
17. Animals at home
22. "That's scalding hot!"
23. Part of a royal flush
24. "Young Frankenstein" role
25. Stick under the seat
26. Knucklehead
27. One, in Germany
28. Puts a stamp on and sends
29. State bordering Montana
30. Comaneci of gymnastics
33. Actress Suvari
34. Part of the eye
35. The basics
37. Disgruntled word
38. "I ___ you're happy!"
40. Ran, like a leaky faucet
41. Person from Tel Aviv, say
42. Tony Blair and Margaret Thatcher, for short
43. ___ and kin
44. Porch on "The Golden Girls"
45. Country whose capital is Cairo
46. Jazz instruments, for short
49. Ivan the Terrible, e.g.
50. Free verse poet ___ Pound
51. Heart-wrenching
52. Gold medal runner Zatopek
53. Fish in a can
54. Irish ___ (meal in Dublin)
57. Critical hosp. area
58. Office computer system

20

Cross Purposes

Across

1 Mont ___ (French mountain)
6 Proof-ending abbr.
9 Goliath's foe
14 Super ___ Bros.
15 America
16 Month before febrero
17 Advice like "Don't fly so low you crash into the Death Star"?
19 Florida animal, for short
20 Drift into dreamland
21 Constellation with a belt
22 Cub Scout leaders, in the UK (hidden in MAKE LAST)
26 Like restaurants that serve sushi, pad thai, and 58-down
29 Do a medical scan on a British royal?
31 ___ Dinh Diem
32 Sports channel
33 Moves, in real estate jargon
34 Diamond or ruby
35 Elected official straight from a Fox singing competition?
39 Not bright
42 In ___ (mad)
43 Apiece
47 ___ Mae Brown (Whoopi Goldberg's "Ghost" role)
48 Resort town for video game enthusiasts?
51 Honorary flag position
53 Wine agent
54 Tinseltown, in headlines
55 Old-school laundry detergent
56 ___ game (chess or Monopoly)
57 Oinker who designed a commercial space shuttle?
63 Highway sign
64 Most common word in English
65 Olympic skater Slutskaya (anagram of IN AIR)
66 "___ to recall..."
67 Animal that says "moo"
68 ___ & Young (accounting firm)

Down

1 Bike race with hills
2 Rule
3 The Diamondbacks, on scoreboards
4 See 10-down
5 Courvoisier or Remy Martin
6 ___ pro quo
7 Unproven ability
8 "___ Kapital"
9 Junior high in a 1980s teen show
10 With 4-down, "Delta of Venus" author
11 Putting the kibosh on
12 Historic period for blacksmiths
13 Palme ___ (Cannes Film Festival prize)
18 "___.0" (Comedy Central webclip show)
21 ___ the other
22 Hatchet
23 ___-One (rapper who guested on R.E.M.'s "Radio Song")
24 "The Raven" monogram
25 Bobcat cousin
26 False reason
27 Permits
28 ___ de guerre
30 Ursus ___ (brown bear)
36 Office machine
37 Equally awful
38 No, to Germans
39 "I blew it," to Homer Simpson
40 Big potatoes
41 Dangerous computer programs
44 Raggedy ___ dolls
45 F/X animation
46 QVC rival
49 Spittoon noise
50 Award for a bad movie
52 Fake a signature
55 Did some sketching
56 Fat measure, for short
57 "The Mayor of Simpleton" band (hidden in NEXT COMES)
58 Saigon soup
59 Slip up
60 Wrestling victory
61 ___ and outs
62 Gangster's sidearm

Come to Your Senses

Across

1 Walk in the Wild West
6 Cleanup crew
11 "Great Expectations" hero
14 Aegean Sea island
15 Mr. Murphy
16 873,254 self-divided
17 Without prior inspection
19 "Great job, Pablo!"
20 Picnic problem
21 Desk item
23 See 4-down
25 Cola wars "battles"
28 Scary-looking lady
29 Guthrie of folk
30 Debtor's ink color, traditionally
31 Financial planner's recommendation
32 Egypt neighbor
34 Grate harshly
38 Parting words
42 Notion
43 Engages in rabble-rousing
44 Chorus syllable
45 Dance style
48 "What ___ is new?"
49 "For ___ a jolly..."
50 Phrase of suspicion
54 Boxer Riddick
55 1982 Masters winner Craig
56 Eye askance
58 Bagel go-with
59 Right of the accused
64 Blow away
65 Actor Davis of "Do the Right Thing"
66 Do the lace over
67 Club ___
68 Frail
69 Washington Post section

Down

1 Hosts
2 "It must be him, ___ shall die" (song lyric)
3 Separate
4 With 23-across, co-director of "True Grit"
5 Himalayan beast of legend
6 Fellas
7 Word with want
8 Cato's clarification
9 One who wins by losing
10 House with 100 people in it
11 Diving places
12 Sea offshoot
13 Jury members
18 Like many rumors
22 Film director Almodóvar
23 Texas treat
24 Put the rowboat in motion
26 Tree of the birch family
27 More sudsy
29 Pop the question
33 ___ Wafers
35 Say-so
36 Tool box object
37 What a teen may go through
39 Satisfied
40 Get cozy
41 Mao ___-tung
46 Totally behind
47 Beggar's cry
50 It was founded in the year 622
51 Harriet Beecher ___
52 Overused the credit card, with "out"
53 Come up
54 Basque cap
57 Eustachian tube homes
60 Free (of)
61 "___ Jude"
62 Nada
63 "Holy Toledo!"

Not Even, Funny!

Across

1 Bakery attraction
6 Kemo ___
10 Where balance is important
14 Necklace item
15 Get ready, for short
16 Beer bash host, maybe
17 Boat with a flat bottom
18 Philosopher Descartes
19 Capture, in chess
20 Odd group that included Sammy Davis, Jr.
23 Puerto ___
26 Small pest
27 "You ___ right!"
28 Rude driver
30 Be a gourmand
32 Salt Lake City gp.
33 Kevin who played a small-screen Hercules
34 Soccer zero
35 Blue ball, in pool
36 Odd group that included Tito
40 Watering hole
41 Not at home
42 Make fit
45 Florida football player, for short
46 Remember the waiter
47 Secret ___ (love-letter writer)
49 "___ if I care!"
51 Part of the hand
53 The Big Apple, on envelopes
54 Odd group that included Tom Hayden
57 Card in a royal flush
58 1980 Olympics host nation
59 Rise
63 Advantage
64 Introduction word
65 Embedded gunk
66 Valentine's Day flower
67 Concordes, e.g.
68 Grouchy "Sesame Street" character

Down

1 "Be on the lookout" message
2 Stephen of the silver screen
3 Rower's need
4 Hershey option
5 Brother of Billy, Daniel, and Stephen Baldwin
6 Jumped (out)
7 NBA game site
8 Actor whose money you could win on a game show
9 Of-fence-ive weapon?
10 Following
11 Ready to go home and relax
12 Gets by
13 Dictation experts
21 Pompousness
22 Back muscle
23 Four Monopoly properties: abbr.
24 Perfect score, as it were
25 "Grand Theft Auto" crimes
29 Ad ___ committee
31 Title sitcom alien
34 "That's ___ funny"
35 Food in a tray
37 It's Japanese for "carp"
38 Hypothesizes
39 "___ the Walrus"
40 Samurai's code of honor
43 Pocket protector item
44 Attempt
45 Source of support
46 Gunpowder or Earl Grey
47 Warnings
48 License givers
50 "Me and Bobby ___"
52 It's no liability
55 Gingivitis spot
56 Downyflake competitor
60 "___-Tac-Dough"
61 Actress Thurman
62 For each

Ghood Ghrief!

Across

1 Billiards tactic
6 Smooth
11 Disparity
14 Former Defense Secretary Les
15 Monotheistic belief
16 Doctors' assn.
17 San Francisco square
19 Dawn personified
20 Not 'neath
21 Blow it
22 Petrol amount
24 "Hold on!"
26 Faked, as in boxing
28 Five Norse kings
31 WWII leader
32 "Yes, We're Open" and "Sorry, We're Closed"
35 Blade brand
37 Start of a Mozart title
40 Repeat, maybe
41 Evil spirit
42 Former despot
43 Tear's partner
44 Billy of rock
45 Violet parts
46 Palindromic time
48 Flood fighter
50 Shocks
53 Owing
57 Gem State capital
58 Leisurely stroll
61 In the style of
62 "___ little teapot..."
63 Autobiographer, often
66 Spy novelist Deighton
67 Left ventricle adjunct
68 "___ we all!"
69 ___ Angeles
70 ___ Hall (New Jersey university)
71 Orphan Annie's dog

Down

1 Cartoon Mr.
2 Pallid
3 Church's peak
4 Knight's title
5 Colors pottery, perhaps
6 Vicious and Caesar
7 Not new
8 ___ a sudden
9 Kilmer of "Top Gun"
10 Estevez of "The Breakfast Club"
11 Restrict to a section of town
12 "That's ___" (Dean Martin hit)
13 Sat for the sculptor
18 Costa ___
23 Employed a syringe
25 Resonant
27 List-ending letters
29 Saudi king
30 Barfly's perch
32 Keep in stitches?
33 Clinch
34 Accra residents
36 Game boundary
38 "Platoon" locale, for short
39 Hosp. sections
41 Actress Lollobrigida
45 Ladies of La Paz
47 Alphas' opposites
49 Penthouse feature
50 Government issue
51 Casanova
52 Curling, say
54 Devoured
55 Mix
56 Cheap and showy, as dress
59 Regarding
60 "The Man" Musial
64 Gardener's tool
65 George Gershwin's brother

You Got Served

Across

1 Show where Alfred helped out
7 Prefix meaning outside
10 Web code
14 Cactus feature
15 Damage the surface
16 Approximately
17 Sneezer's need
18 Seafood delicacies
20 U.S. immigrant's class
21 Title sitcom character who wrote in a diary at the end of each show
23 Tailor's stitch
25 "Are you?" answer
26 Composer Stravinsky
29 Makes tea
33 Houston sports venue that opened in 1965
38 ___-tzu
39 Show where Lurch answered with "You rang?"
43 "___ the land of the free..."
44 Units equal to 0.3527 ounces
45 Oldest "Brady Bunch" girl
49 ___ fixe
50 "O, Canada" is one
53 Dummy
57 Show where Tony Danza played a housekeeper named...Tony
62 ___ Palmas
63 Does better than, in competition
64 Type of test
66 Ballet burst
67 TV "Science Guy" Bill
68 Peter of "Lawrence of Arabia"
69 Stench
70 Author Brown
71 TV butler who eventually becomes lieutenant governor

Down

1 Maine college
2 Get up
3 Inventor Nikola
4 Calendar pages: abbr.
5 Reunion attendee
6 ___-do-well
7 Host the event
8 ___ Jr. (burger chain)
9 "Storms of Life" country singer Randy
10 Line in love stories
11 Bird's home
12 Catholic title, for short
13 Come up short
19 Play, as bongo drums
22 Scenic route path
24 Actress Sorvino
27 Zeus or Poseidon
28 Like almost all prime numbers
30 Director Kazan
31 ___ trees (sight in Hawaii)
32 Some milk sources
33 Microscopic bit
34 Stadium where Jim Bunning pitched a perfect game
35 Dakota, once: abbr.
36 Mrs., in Montmartre
37 Language where the number of words for "snow" is debated
40 Pet Rocks or Virtual Pets, e.g.
41 Become better, like cheddar
42 Wilbur's horse
46 Non-scary ghost
47 Like Olympic competitions: abbr.
48 Within reach
51 Outkast hit song
52 Buddy of "The Beverly Hillbillies"
54 "Miami Vice" actor Edward James ___
55 Sao ___, Brazil
56 German industrial city
57 "Barney Miller" character
58 Many-___ (multicolored)
59 Bus driver on "The Simpsons"
60 Neatnik's nightmare roommate
61 Construction location
65 Heavy weight

Let's Make a Deal

Across

1 "Wheel of Fortune" host
6 Fancy parties
11 ___ Solo ("Star Wars" role)
14 In unison
15 Animal of the Andes
16 Driving force
17 Sun-Tzu's classic treatise
19 Prepare to fire
20 Space Shuttle org.
21 Alfalfa's sweetheart on "The Little Rascals"
23 Slowpokes
27 Overly formal
29 Beatles song from "The White Album"
30 Some Arabs
32 Northern European language
34 Run casually
35 Lady's secret, perhaps
38 Lacking life
39 Word with mirror or graven
41 Off in the distance
42 Dollar rival
43 Petty quarrel
44 Type of kiss or pie
46 Rulers of the heavens
49 Beat
50 Stop sign's shape
52 Common cuisine
54 Soup base
55 Use a ewer
56 Eternity, seemingly
57 London landmark
64 ___-fi (literary genre)
65 Remove data
66 Ontario tribe members
67 Computer key
68 New car nightmares
69 Wives of knights

Down

1 Approached the bench?
2 Fireplace bit
3 Average guy
4 Santa ___, Calif.
5 Popcorn-to-be
6 Like some magazine covers
7 ___-Romeo (Italian car company)
8 Alan Dershowitz's field
9 Simon and Garfunkel's "I ___ Rock"
10 Canned fish
11 John Ritter TV show
12 Good at gymnastics, maybe
13 Desert wanderer
18 Road gunk
22 Will Smith role
23 Watergate figure G. Gordon ___
24 Not in the dark
25 Bar order
26 Flippant
27 Big-city blight
28 Sioux shelter
31 Send to cloud nine
33 Conscious of, slangily
36 John Lennon's "Mind ___"
37 Wear away, as a coastline
40 Principal
41 Related by blood
43 Saw
45 "Shaken, not ___" (James Bond line)
47 Enjoy eggs
48 Sportscaster's info
50 Stout
51 Comfy shoes
53 Center
55 Annoying type
58 Mined material
59 Sickly pale
60 Lyricist Gershwin
61 Like romantic lights
62 Beaver Cleaver's exclamation
63 Curvy letter

You Better Shape Up

Across

1 ___ Diego
4 Fit for a king
9 Tough days at the plate
14 "Go, bullfighter!"
15 One of the nine Muses
16 Deck that includes The Hanged Man
17 506, in ancient Rome
18 Impromptu musical gatherings
20 Mustard family flower
22 "Yeah, right!"
23 Verily
24 Tiny, as portions go
28 "___ the eggman..." (Beatles line)
29 Crowd cheer
32 Arouse, as anger
33 They're used in scrimshaw
37 Russian parliament
38 ___ and haw
39 Radio "Doctor" known for offbeat music
41 ___ Lingus
42 Genesis name
44 Chop shop inventory
46 Historic record
48 ___ Lanka
49 Language suffix
50 Big name in toilet cleaners
52 Twisted Sister frontman Dee
55 Audience sounds
57 "Here lies..." statement
58 Enemy in a They Might Be Giants song
62 Mil. designation
63 ___ Carlo
64 Getting older
65 Pro opposite
66 "The Simpsons" mouse
67 Pizza order, with "the"
68 Summertime, in St-Tropez

Down

1 Phrase of agreement
2 Dance legend Ailey
3 "Sweet Caroline" singer
4 Cashed in coupons
5 Screwed up
6 Tasteless ornamentation
7 It may only give twenties
8 Central sites
9 Actress Meryl
10 Specialty dairy brand
11 www.ilovebacon.com, e.g.
12 "The Simpsons" bartender
13 You get three for an FG
19 Company called "Big Blue"
21 Circus animal
25 Where you swing your partner
26 "Serpico" director Sidney
27 Word after dog or leap
29 Carefree runs
30 Lend ___ (listen)
31 Art giant Matisse
33 Common crop
34 Funny Youngman
35 Wanna-___ (poseurs)
36 Sault ___ Marie, Mich.
40 Job seeker's list
43 Rest day
45 ___ were (so to speak)
47 Adjective for Bugs and Daffy
51 Lumberjack's product
52 Punish corporally
53 Orlando's ___ Center
54 Arles' river
56 Cole ___ (KFC side)
57 Muslim ruler
58 "That's more than I needed to know" abbr.
59 Go bad
60 Company letters
61 Inflatable trait

Final Destinations

Across

1 Actor Murphy of "Trading Places"
6 Hooded snake
11 Letters before I
14 One-eyed "Futurama" character
15 Tangerine-grapefruit hybrids
16 Football coach Parseghian
17 Like some monologues
18 Mozart's music
20 1988 hit for The Cure
22 Orange ender
23 ___-cone (carnival purchase)
24 Pinochle plays
26 Reindeer gathering
28 Subject of debate
32 ___ Valley, Calif.
33 Busy mo. for CPAs
35 The Piltdown Man, for one
37 It may need a cover sheet
38 Fun for tourists in the Caribbean
42 Folds or Stiller
43 Leave at the altar
44 Compass dir: abbr.
45 Bumbling people
47 Boy Scout Jamboree unit
49 Part of TLC
53 Book with Boise and Bavaria
55 Ending for web or video
57 Apiece
58 1960s protester's chant
63 Comfy kind of sofa
64 Handle an axe
65 Paintings, sculpture, etc.
66 Large-scale
67 Come after
68 Functional start?
69 Mattress cover
70 Hotel postings

Down

1 "The Lord of the Rings" star Wood
2 Strip away, as a forest
3 More concentrated, as population
4 "How did ___ that happen?"
5 Viscounts' superiors
6 Bird that pops out on the hour
7 Give the eye
8 Drab
9 Get up
10 Indian state near the Himalayas
11 Skin tightener
12 Their kids have kids
13 Computer that sang "Daisy"
19 Folk singer Burl
21 Music at the beginning of a service
25 High roll on a die
27 Hydroelectric power site
29 Picture
30 Saturn model
31 Dupe
34 Sandwich sometimes served crustless, for short
36 Signs quickly
38 Like overly tanned skin
39 Changes one's tone of voice
40 "As seen on TV" metal cleaner
41 "Hold on a ___!"
42 Snake that'll put a squeeze on you
46 Pepper's pal
48 South American wildcat
50 Most fitting
51 Affix anew
52 Deteriorates
54 ___ down (sheds weight)
56 Groundskeeper's tool
59 Ark captain
60 Not twice
61 Ending for share or free
62 One of Columbus's ships
63 Lamentable

Current Events

Across

1 Deli spread
5 "The Chronicles of Narnia" author C. S.
10 On the ___ (fleeing)
13 Jazz's state
14 "___ to Hold Your Hand"
15 Journalist Pauley
16 "Cheers" regular
17 Bother
18 Pitching successes
19 Rajiv Gandhi's mother
21 Causes great anguish to
23 Copycat
25 English noblewoman's address
26 Order in the court?
29 "What did I tell you?"
30 Former Russian ruler
31 Sisters
33 Prima donna's favorite numbers
37 Prefix with space or plane
38 Lacking originality
40 Dog name
41 Thanksgiving table item
43 List-ending abbreviation
44 Half a sestet
45 Greek goddess of the dawn
47 Republican symbol
49 Prepare leftovers
52 Anti-flooding device
53 Of the heavens
55 Mr. Schwarzenegger
59 Element #26
60 So far
62 Brainstorm
63 Pulitzer-winning musical of 1996
64 ___ Island
65 Laundry amount
66 Actor Billy ___ Williams
67 "Green Eggs and Ham" author
68 Goes wrong

Down

1 1936 Pasteur portrayer Paul
2 "This must weigh ___!"
3 Furlong fraction
4 Electrician's favorite TV show?
5 Connective tissue
6 She bleats
7 Electrician's verbal shrug?
8 Fascinated by
9 Weather map features
10 Actress Dern
11 Put in one's two cents?
12 Like a teen's room, stereotypically
15 Electrician's favorite movie?
20 South American metropolis, familiarly
22 Draws
24 Get accustomed
26 Party type
27 Consumer
28 Silents star Theda ___
32 Like an old joke
34 Pre-euro money
35 Chief Norse god
36 Chimney sweep's covering
39 Puts on a pedestal
42 Not my
46 Obsolete weaponry
48 A pop
49 Out there
50 "___ Grows in Brooklyn"
51 Avignon's river
54 Late tennis star Arthur
56 Stench
57 King of Shakespeare
58 Pops
61 Bradley and Meese

The Bachelor Ate

Across

1 "Dick Tracy" role
5 Botanical ring
11 Rx givers
14 Hawaiian island
15 Marvin Gaye classic "___ Healing"
16 Alley ___
17 Dinner you can't mess up
19 Codebreaking arm of govt.
20 Lack of comfort
21 Little piggy, really
22 Clapton on guitar
23 Emperor who fiddled while Rome burned
25 ___ solution (contact lens wearers use it)
27 Welsh form of the name John
30 "Michael Collins" actor Stephen
33 New York parade store
34 Breakfast you can't mess up
38 Mel of home run fame
39 Those hurt, as by crime
40 DJ's crateful
43 Lunch you can't mess up
46 Boise's state
48 Period for historians
49 Kyrgyzstan's continent
50 Give in
52 Mean words
55 Land in the ocean
56 Letters after Q
59 Relatives created at weddings
63 "Do you get it?"
64 Midnight snack you can't mess up
66 Slip
67 Collision type
68 Newspaper piece
69 Pig's home
70 Makes tank-like
71 Neighbor of Earth

Down

1 Protein source for vegans
2 Have coming
3 Sock cover
4 Journey hit of 1986
5 Actor Ed
6 House member, for short
7 Go out
8 Greek booze
9 Guards the couch
10 Pie ___ mode
11 Comedian with a role in "Casino"
12 Like a violinist's strings
13 Word dividers
18 Ending for legal or Senegal
22 Israeli airline
24 Source of wisdom
26 Pennsylvania group
27 Prefix meaning "green"
28 Puppy doc
29 Site of a painter's show
31 Go in
32 Sneaker brand
35 Par ___ (via air mail)
36 Tiny
37 2100, in Roman numerals
41 Next-to-last Greek letter
42 Caribbean or Caspian
44 First president of South Korea
45 Noble's domain
46 Pretty flowers
47 Sahara or Mojave
51 More sincere
53 Detroit team
54 It's one for Mexicans
57 It may say "HOT STOCK TIP!!!!"
58 Chore list header
60 Jessica of "Dark Angel"
61 "Dead Poets Society" director Peter
62 Fast jets, for short
64 Half a dance step
65 It goes with neither

Telling Left From Right

Across

1 Arabian peninsula country that sounds like a 1960s exclamation

5 Suffix for pay

8 Dine al fresco, maybe

14 Plato of "Diff'rent Strokes"

15 It can be made or poked

16 Like daredevils, if they give a thumbs-up

17 Bugs

18 Last cop to issue a parking ticket?

20 Pastry shop puffs

22 United group

23 Tickled doll

24 Little bit, in French

25 Rubber-stamped

28 Org. for good putters

30 What Benedict XVI's documents are written on?

33 Saturn model

34 Cholesterol varieties

35 Movie critic Joel

37 ___ Wafers

39 Nine-digit ID

41 Thin and fragile

42 Off the water

44 Univ., sometimes

46 T-shirt size: abbr.

47 Huge pile of locker-room laundry?

49 "Star Trek: Voyager" character (hidden in LAKESIDE)

50 Planetoid

51 Ending for north or northwest

52 Church area

54 Waffle grabbed in ads

56 Brand in the cleaning aisle

59 Mess up a mathematician by shouting random numbers?

63 Peter and Ray's ghost-busting partner

64 "___ Rouge!" (Nicole Kidman movie)

65 It's between Can. and Mex.

66 Yield

67 Fails to

68 Comes down with

69 ___ Kringle (Santa Claus)

Down

1 Garfield's foil

2 Clothing designer ___ Jacobs

3 Navy tattoo near your foot?

4 Like the "ng" sound

5 ATV's destination

6 Guzman of "Traffic"

7 Landers of advice

8 Exercises done with a bar

9 Facts

10 City near Springfield, MA

11 Cloister sister

12 Intense anger

13 Middle pt.

19 Cain's victim

21 Beseech

24 ___ fruit

26 Beer bash with pelvic exercises?

27 Coat with flour

28 ___ colada

29 Seeks out

31 Polite shorthand abbr.

32 Drain diverter

36 Soap ingredients

38 Clanky instruments

40 Weather report abbr.

43 High-class

45 Mesdames, in Mexico

48 Beat a path

53 Sweater cut

55 Killer Ed who inspired "Psycho" (anagram of INGE)

56 Elevated flattop

57 Creedence Clearwater Revival classic

58 Change for a five

59 Makers of the Athlon processor

60 Scooby-___ (TV dog)

61 Word on bills

62 "You didn't know that?"

Splitsville

Across

1 Politically correct pronoun

6 U can follow them

9 Pile

13 Survey choice, sometimes

14 Stadium demolished in 2009

15 World's Fair word

16 Bread choice

18 Facades

19 School period

20 It beats, working

21 Prurient interest

22 Cry to the toreador

23 He broke Lou's consecutive games record

24 Quaker food

26 Some family tree members

31 Be a bad houseguest

34 Marge and Homer's middle child

35 House vote

36 Enjoys, as benefits

37 Wine container

38 One brick shy of a load

40 First name in advice

41 "Woe is me!"

43 Lose it

44 Rodeo participant

47 Stray dog, often

48 Ladies of the house

49 Play copycat

52 Three-card monte, notably

54 ___-Kettering Institute

57 Karras of "Webster"

58 Foil-wrapped chocolate treat

59 Quaver, in music

61 Actor Sharif

62 Razor brand

63 Cyberspace

64 New England team, for short

65 Drive's start

66 Kitchen riser

Down

1 Do-it-yourselfer's bookstore section

2 Singer Merman

3 Coast

4 Captain's spot

5 Before

6 Carla on "Cheers"

7 Brown meat

8 Parlor acquisitions

9 Wellness

10 Comment to a burper

11 Many N.Y.C. homes

12 Jerusalem newspaper

14 Pantry division

17 Seek blubber

23 "The Cup of Tea" painter Mary

25 Speechless

26 '50s dance

27 Get red

28 Fix, as an outcome

29 Best Musical of 1995-6

30 Gives an opinion

31 Turkey neighbor

32 Bill of fare

33 Tropics headgear

37 Jolt

39 Unified

42 "Dig in!"

43 Johnson's successor

45 Neil Simon play

46 Missouri River city

49 Honolulu howdy

50 "For ___ sake!"

51 Exercise, as influence

52 Hit the mall

53 Deep sleep

55 Dietetic, in ad-speak

56 Beast

57 Prefix with chamber or bellum

60 "Yo!"

Roll Call

Across

1 Based on base eight
6 "___ Good Men"
10 Headline
14 Weeper of myth
15 Welles' tycoon publisher
16 Flash or sugar follower
17 "The Great Forest" painter Max
18 A couple of rolls
20 Hankering
21 George Bush was one
22 It's distilled from wine
23 Two more rolls
26 Suitable
27 Clunky dory
28 As attentive as Ross Perot?
32 Grim Grimm guys
35 Scottish terrier
37 Coiled choker
38 Three more rolls
42 Cool, in the '50s
43 Warmonger
44 Tipped rapiers
45 Scorpio's brightest
48 Rock and Roll Hall of Fame architect
49 Pier gp.
50 Yet another two rolls
56 Recently
59 Animal house
60 Counter's opener
61 The last two rolls
63 Picture
64 "Out of Africa" author Dinesen
65 "Breathless" star Richard
66 Rather risky
67 1169 erupter
68 Symbols of strength
69 Palette pigment

Down

1 Get the better of
2 Wispy clouds
3 The Friendly Islands
4 No-show
5 "___ the Good Times Roll"
6 Cub Scout pack leader
7 "Oliver Twist" baddie
8 He was attached to his brother
9 Friday on TV
10 Predicament
11 Lazy Susan
12 Sacked out
13 Put your money (on)
19 Sea east of the Caspian
21 Go with the flow, perhaps
24 Unseat
25 Rapids transit
29 Moon unit?
30 Characterization
31 Pipes up
32 Workplace watchdog: abbr.
33 "Damn Yankees" dancer Verdon
34 Cold-bloodedly treacherous
35 Cash cache
36 Royal Botanic Gardens site
39 "___ Bop" ('84 Cyndi Lauper hit)
40 Scoff
41 Contagious, as laughter
46 Baked state?
47 Compile a top-ten list
48 Cutesy trailer
51 Country rock's ___ Mountain Daredevils
52 "The Highwayman" poet Alfred
53 Gunslinger's command
54 Fastidious Felix
55 Skeptical response from the Cyclops?
56 "The Grapes of Wrath" figure
57 Firmly fixed
58 Hence
62 Kind of nut or brain
63 Veiled comment?

Tops

Across

1 Climbs
6 They're radio-active
10 Altar area
14 Scrub, NASA-style
15 Moises of baseball
16 Climb
17 Historic Alabama city
18 Sylvester's trademark
19 Lohengrin's bride
20 Top choice
23 Target the target
24 Deposited
25 Blow it
26 Cartoon collectible
28 "Sweater Girl" Turner
30 Third numero
32 Am-scray, old-style
34 Gushes
37 Bedevil
38 Top dog
42 Throw around
43 Largest city of the West Indies
44 Stage whispers
46 It isn't gross
47 Ivory source
51 Machine gun syllable
52 Give the go-ahead
54 Cash register co.
56 Herd word
57 Top deb
61 Cubist Joan
62 Without question
63 Ho Chi Minh city
64 Goody two shoes
65 "Let Us Now Praise Famous Men" author James
66 Vacuum tube gas
67 Down Under greeting
68 It's a question of time
69 Dill swill

Down

1 Scamp
2 Airline to Madrid
3 Extremely earnest
4 Anecdotal Bombeck
5 It's canceled when it's accepted
6 Twice-told, it's still a tale
7 Came down to earth
8 Israeli statesman Dayan
9 Splendiferous
10 Antiquing element
11 Explorer Marco's outerwear?
12 Hitchcock's genre
13 Pollution police: abbr.
21 ____-body experience
22 Blockhead
27 Unwelcome glance
29 Invited
31 Hawke of "Reality Bites"
33 Imply
35 Gulf War general
36 Girls' magazine
38 H.S. exam
39 "Superman" intro phrase
40 Yardsticks
41 Glom (onto)
45 It has its ups and downs
48 African river
49 Oater bar
50 Tiger great Al
53 Hard-nosed
55 Post-op therapy
58 Sluggish
59 Complimentary
60 Roseanne, once
61 Fuel economy letters

Possibility Thinking

Across

1 Terrific, in Hollywoodese
6 Hercule's creator
12 Hit on the head
15 Beaver State capital
16 Hold up
17 Harvard or Yale
18 Quip by Dr. Andrew S. Tanenbaum, part 1
20 Square dancer, perhaps
21 Put two and two together
22 Kindergarten breaks
23 Come unexpectedly (onto)
25 "The Producers" star Zero
27 "The Last Tycoon" director Kazan
28 Quip, part 2
32 Nirvana
33 One way up the slope
34 Diner drink
36 Melodies
37 Quip, part 3
40 Windfall
41 FDR's successor
42 Cuatro y cuatro
43 Sighed with delight
44 Quip, part 4
49 CEO, often
50 Like Bowls and All-Star games
51 Name meaning "heavenly"
54 Extension extension
55 Tiny toiler
58 Breakfast of gladiators?
59 End of quip
62 Snapshot
63 Founder of est
64 Too-too
65 Draft choice
66 Marshmallow munchies
67 "The Volcano Lover" novelist Sontag

Down

1 Jet set jets
2 Surfing Shangri-la
3 Skelton's Kadiddlehopper
4 Starr in the news
5 Inauspicious
6 Whizzes
7 Starter's words
8 AAU member
9 Mai ___ (cocktails)
10 Alluded to
11 Bony
12 1961 Jimmy Dean chart-topper
13 Horse course
14 "Here Is Your War" author Ernie
19 Threw or throw
24 Russian for "peace"
25 It grows on trees
26 Slate backing
28 Select group
29 Mecca, to Muhammad
30 Court org.
31 County fair cry
32 "Faugh!"
35 His job is on the line
37 Winter disturbance
38 ___ Na Na
39 1/3 of a WWII movie
40 Jezebel's deity
42 Son of Agamemnon
43 Mozart's middle name
45 Bard's before
46 "More! More!"
47 Hair holders
48 Willa Cather's "One of ___"
51 Lola's club of song
52 Blackhearted
53 Off-the-wall feedback?
55 College knowledge
56 "Sleepless in Seattle" director Ephron
57 Fed
60 Kramden laugh syllable
61 Bug with two homonyms

Pink Ladies

Across

1 Ring king with a sting
4 Totem, beforehand
9 Take over for
14 Chinese discipline
15 "The ___ Hilton" ('87 war movie)
16 Mischief maker
17 Powerful stuff
18 "Pinky" Oscar nominee
20 Baby blues
22 "Peggy Sue" singer
23 Some VCRs
24 Efficient way to work
26 Classical beginning
28 "Pretty in Pink" star
34 Monet or Debussy
36 A hundred sawbucks
37 "Luck ___ Lady Tonight"
38 John Cougar's "___ So Good"
39 Hearty "har"
40 Get Mad all over again
42 UN member since 1949
43 Gulf north of Somalia
45 Shakes in one's boots
46 "Pink Motel" star
49 Bar passer: abbr.
50 ___ to the bar
53 Back a baddie
56 Top-40 DJ Casey
59 One and only
60 "Heller in Pink Tights" star
63 Christopher Carson, familiarly
64 Sing like the birdies sing
65 Pen or pin follower
66 Hagen of "Reversal of Fortune"
67 Quick on the uptake
68 Stow the dough
69 Brooks of "Blazing Saddles"

Down

1 Early Mexican
2 "Semi-Tough" actress Lotte
3 Bring two families together, perhaps
4 Most commonly used word in English
5 Dirty digs
6 Wicked
7 French Christmas
8 Stop, as a story
9 Splashy resort
10 NASCAR service area
11 Biz biggie
12 Old Italian money
13 More, to a minimalist
19 Crossword puzzle inventor Arthur
21 Gush
25 Seadog
27 Chinese menu item
29 Roly-poly
30 It may be invisible
31 Comics rube
32 Satyr's stare
33 Butler who spoke for Yogi Bear and Huckleberry Hound
34 Flake
35 Elbow-bender
39 "Certainly!"
41 Tom of "The Seven Year Itch"
44 He's coached Bears and Saints
45 Twain, actually
47 Tizzy
48 Spain plus Portugal
51 Band together
52 Bit of a bloom
53 Charles barker
54 Rose or Orange
55 Rapier relative
57 Matterhorn milieu
58 The black in the stack
61 Addams family cousin
62 Extreme degree

Meet the Flintstones

Across

1 Undermines the foundation
5 ___-Ray discs
8 Cause and ___
14 Run for the stables
15 LBJ follower
16 "Starlight Express" director Nunn
17 *Gigantic bird with a stone passenger cab
19 *Item with an image-chiseling bird
20 Ending for classic or violin
21 Year, in Spanish
22 Gloom
23 *Musical item using a pointy-beaked bird
28 Eye part
29 Birds found on Australian ranches
30 Wrap something up
33 "Ad ___ per aspera" (Kansas' state motto)
35 PBS kids' show that taught Ubby-Dubby
36 Company head
37 *Signalling item, when the bird's tail is pulled
39 *Motorist's signal, when the bird is squeezed
42 Wish you could take back
43 "Sesame Street" muppet
45 "Biography" network
46 "Absolutely!"
47 Earth goddess
48 Other, to Oswaldo
49 *Garden tool, when the bird's legs are squeezed
53 "This ___ the record"
55 Dig in
56 Radio host Glass
57 *Writing implement using a bird's beak
59 *Talking bird flying back and forth between stone boxes
61 Shirt part
62 "Little piggy," really
63 "___ but known...."
64 Plays with, like a puppy
65 AMA members
66 A matador hears them

Down

1 Step
2 Get out of bed
3 Baltimore and New Orleans
4 NASCAR sponsor
5 Uses a hot iron, as on cattle
6 Quick stretch in "The Alphabet Song"
7 Article written by Voltaire?
8 What the king keeps saying in "The King and I"
9 Sets up to take the blame
10 Thigh bone
11 At any time
12 Champagne stopper
13 Singing syllable
18 Cowboy's rope
24 Hockey great Bobby and others
25 "Titanic" actor DiCaprio
26 Shell alternative
27 "Arizona City," since 1873
30 Cost-friendly
31 Geeky type
32 Cooked
33 Off-kilter
34 Elisabeth of "Leaving Las Vegas"
35 Woody Allen title role of 1984
38 Heavy metal
40 Ostrich or kiwi, e.g.
41 Do damage to
44 West of Hollywood
47 Swiss city, or its lake
48 Takes to the soapbox
49 JFK's were high
50 Kind of voice
51 Etch away
52 Director of "Caddyshack" and "Analyze This"
53 "To Live and Die ___"
54 Twist stats
57 You need one to get online
58 Tennis barrier
59 "___ be an honor!"
60 Sorority letter

Cyberdorks

Across

1. "___ extra charge"
5. It'll get you to the top of a mountain
9. Tennis champ Monica
14. Bangle bit
15. Hanger material
16. German WWI sub
17. Film legend who measured old modems?
20. Davis of "Do the Right Thing"
21. Dull shades
22. Golf appointment
24. "Talk of the Nation" airer
25. Utah campus, for short
28. Stacked item in a cafeteria
29. Space traveler who types in "http"?
32. Nut used in soft drinks
33. Actress Meg and pitcher Nolan
34. 1980s pop star who surfs the Net a lot?
38. Top-quality
40. Have ___ (be torn, as jeans)
41. Boxer who uses an operating system?
44. Singer/actor Kristofferson
48. Med. condition that often involves cleaning
49. Irritate
50. Military base near Washington, D.C.
52. Copenhagen gardens
54. Varnish stuff
55. Poet who corresponds often?
59. Clothing attachment
60. Not new, like a car
61. ___ mater
62. Brother: Fr.
63. Be bratty
64. Eliot ___ (Kevin Costner role of 1987)

Down

1. Costello's comedy partner
2. Pre-release video
3. Sick feeling
4. Strange fact
5. Airline no more
6. With lasting resentment
7. Section
8. Moved the picture to a different room, e.g.
9. Non-slip product description
10. Declines
11. Singer Reed
12. Tinnitus spot
13. RR stop
18. Outdoor goods retailer
19. Early baseball Hall-of-Famer ___ Rixey (anagram of PAPE)
23. Lepton family particle
25. Victoria's Secret buys
26. Yang's counterpart
27. Wee-___ (kids)
30. 1980s-90's show with Jimmy Smits
31. "Atlas Shrugged" author Rand
32. Tennessee city
34. Three of a ___
35. Bug-eyed bird
36. Openings
37. Upshot
38. Mideast gp.
39. Rocker Ocasek
42. "A Mighty Wind" actor Eugene
43. 1960 Paul Newman movie set in Biblical times
44. "Dr. Strangelove" actor Wynn
45. Take to the ground, in the hills
46. Turns of phrase
47. Flowering plants of the tropics
51. Hosp. scanner
52. Stadium section
53. Singer/guitarist Loeb
55. Seasonal mall worker
56. Taint
57. Bart Simpson's grandpa
58. Sorts: abbr.

Safe!

Across

1 ___ up (come clean)
5 Business biggie
9 Business biggie
14 Gangplank
15 Betting setting
16 In concert
17 Friendly leader?
18 Subterranean soldiers
19 Danish currency
20 "Your secret's safe!"
23 Ganges port NW of Calcutta
24 North of Virginia
25 Wrestle (with)
28 Builder's backing
32 With 43-Across, "I'm safe!"
35 Asylum seeker
37 Bemoan
38 Ballad
39 Palindromic rock video award
40 Where It. is
41 Croatian capital
43 See 32-Across
45 Any of three English rivers
46 Dr. Edwards' "Spellbound" malady
48 Women of distinction
50 Carve up
54 "It's safe!"
59 Outpouring
60 Bat Masterson's weapon
61 Imposter
62 What's happening
63 Wide-eyed
64 Kiln kin
65 Nosy Parker
66 Jay with a jaw
67 1996 Tony-winning musical

Down

1 Shabby individual
2 Grade made in the shade?
3 Make iron into steel
4 Resilient
5 Big times?
6 Lawless character
7 Thermodynamic disorganization
8 "I Never Played the Game" author Howard
9 George of "Star Trek"
10 Amos Oz, for one
11 Cat's-paw
12 Bancroft of "The Graduate"
13 Cry out for
21 Hood release?
22 Places for aces?
26 "Sweet Home ___"
27 Layer
29 "Happy Days Are Here Again" composer Milton
30 "___ Colors" (Cyndi Lauper chart-topper)
31 In plain sight
32 Pasta that looks like rice
33 Pig-out party
34 Staying power, in "Variety"
36 Wild and crazy guy
39 Sharp feller
42 Minimal moolah
43 Playing one's part
44 Buy, so to speak
47 Peyote
49 It's from the heart
51 Hit the road
52 Like a bucket in an 1843 song
53 Dickens' Little Nell ___
54 Parker of "South Park"
55 Teeming multitude
56 Square
57 Cognizant of
58 Utah's state flower

A Visit to Three States

Across

1 Trade
5 Pop
9 Nomad's transport
14 Beach plaything
15 Range dividing Europe and Asia
16 Computer company
17 "M*A*S*H" actor
18 Famous fiddler
19 Block, perhaps
20 Took risks
23 Rowboat needs
24 One, in France
25 Refined
28 Where people get pumped
30 Terrific person
33 Time-tested tune
34 Like people from Bangkok
35 Sport played on horseback
36 Falls apart under scrutiny
39 Flying annoyance
40 Women hate it when they run
41 Woody Allen movie of 1990
42 Slippery sort
43 Sulk in silence
44 House sellers
45 Cigarette package word
46 Brewskis
47 Releasing pent-up emotion
55 "Rosemary's Baby" author Ira
56 Schnozz stimulus
57 In neutral
58 Javelin or epee
59 Old Italian bread?
60 Simon of the stage
61 Eats poshly
62 Stable diet?
63 Word with tight or split

Down

1 Slimming-down places
2 Put on first, maybe
3 Verdi work
4 Aristotle, for one
5 Miscellaneous
6 Milk accompaniment
7 "Shucks!"
8 Oodles
9 Summer camp accommodations
10 Make up (for)
11 Ankle-length dress
12 ___ the Red (Norwegian explorer)
13 Checkout headache
21 Put away
22 Like some summer days
25 Avoid
26 Flying solo
27 Perfect
28 Whoopi's Oscar movie
29 Where Bill and Hillary met
30 Gained admission
31 Campaign sign word
32 Societal customs
34 Grand
35 Middle East region
37 Nettlesome issue
38 Union concern
43 Emulates El Greco
44 "Batman" butler
45 Tough string
46 Prior to, dialectically
47 Reacted to being cut
48 Strauss of jeans
49 Kitchen feature
50 Wherein Woods uses woods
51 "Garfield" character
52 Place of temptation
53 "Put ___ on it!"
54 Gibson and Brooks of Hollywood

Four for Fore

Across

1 They're often covered with baby food
5 "The Human Comedy" author
11 Sporty British car, for short
14 Lazing about
15 "My Favorite Year" star
16 Cousin of org, com, and net
17 "Rebel Without a Cause" actress
19 Fish eggs
20 Eliot's "___ Marner"
21 1984 World Series champs
23 Feminist Gloria
26 John, Paul, George and Ringo
27 Route to the roof
28 In need of calories
31 Sigourney Weaver flick
32 Not too shabby
33 Latvia's capital
36 Get benched
37 Tulsa residents, e.g.
40 Sought office
41 Sarcastic laugh
43 Barney's buddy
44 Rainbow or lake, e.g.
46 Made shine
48 Medal metal
49 Underworld figure
51 Doesn't just brush
52 What some graduate with
54 Bias
55 Billy Joel's "Don't ___ Me Why"
56 "Clue" suspect
61 Forego folding
62 Relaxed, on base
63 Goad
64 Blow it
65 Decades, to centuries
66 Kitty comment

Down

1 Recycling container
2 Ore. neighbor
3 Diner order
4 Coast
5 Big water heater
6 2010 action movie, with "The"
7 Meteorologist's predictions
8 Lion's home, maybe
9 Bunches
10 Giving up
11 Best Actor of 1990
12 Love to pieces
13 Shot in the dark
18 Content of some closets
22 Teri of "Young Frankenstein"
23 Cut drastically, as prices
24 Actress Shire
25 Archie's mate
28 Gave an edge to
29 "Previously owned," in ad-speak
30 Neither here ___ there
32 Achy
34 Bandage material
35 Primes the pot
38 Not working
39 Pungent
42 Wheels
45 Speaker's platform
47 Structure
48 Turns the music way up
49 Step
50 Unfortunate fellow
51 ___ and blood (kin)
53 Spot
54 "ER" command
57 D.C. figure
58 Before
59 This may be inflated
60 Improved partner

Meet the Press

Across

1. Gets hard
5. "Freeze!"
9. "Gonna Fly Now" flick
14. Actor's accessory
15. Baum barker
16. "Tomorrow" show
17. Their work is taxing
19. Coup group
20. Giant "Arabian Nights" flyer
21. Pieces for Pavarotti
23. Denver Broncos nickname
25. Like Chianti and Chablis
28. It may need massaging
29. Milan opera house
31. Use a dragnet
34. High-rise support
36. Psych final?
37. Creamy-white winter veggie
40. ___ facto
41. Name in a Salinger title
42. Carpi connectors
43. Show how it happened
45. "So there!"
46. They pull in pushers: abbr.
47. Steady
53. Designs on you, perhaps
54. Brine-cured salmon
55. "Stop already!"
58. La Salle named it and claimed it for France
60. Party handout
61. Meir contemporary
62. Spring (from)
63. "The Party's Over" composer Jule
64. It's outstanding
65. Myra of the piano

Down

1. Veep after Hubert
2. Diamond flaw?
3. Puccini's titular soprano
4. You may get into hot water here
5. Sound investment?
6. Pick-me-up
7. "The Wind in the Willows" character
8. Put forth, as an axiom
9. Bombay bigwigs
10. Blame
11. "Crossfire" network
12. Craft shop buy
13. Shout of approval
18. Grounded skein
22. Peter and Paul, but not Mary
24. "Queen of Hearts" singer Juice
25. Old Nick name?
26. "Aeneid" queen
27. Apt rhyme for "stash"
30. Washington's Grand dam
31. Beach Boys' "Fun, Fun, Fun" car
32. Kashmir cash
33. Discombobulated
34. Gradually implanted
35. "Hallelujah, I'm a ___"
38. Hit the high points
39. Bank hold-ups?
44. Current bit
45. Strain to see
48. Mythical weeper
49. Four-week-old pigeon
50. Send sky-high
51. City subdivisions
52. They're held for questioning
53. Stratford's stream
55. Contingencies
56. Goon's gun
57. College growth?
59. Fin or Finn follower

Joint Chiefs

Across

1 Basket boundary
4 Unreleased, as emotion
10 Start for a playwright
14 Turkish title
15 Get excited
16 First word of two Springsteen albums
17 Person who hauls shrubbery?
19 "Beat it!"
20 Count in music
21 "Exodus" author
23 Ending for lemon or lime
24 Properly organized
27 Consoling one
29 Not nuts
30 Jamaican export
32 Boot the dictator
33 Punish a speeder, perhaps
34 Where people nosh
35 Federal money for a project?
41 Lucy's sidekick
42 Falco of "Nurse Jackie"
43 Coral reefs
45 Nancy's husband
46 "Make a ___!"
50 Vote back into office
52 "Desperately Seeking Susan" star Arquette
54 Suffix with hobby or lobby
55 Campus quarters
57 Giant
58 French 101 verb
60 Grab some market share from an auto company?
63 Goblet feature
64 Relax
65 Tiger Woods tool
66 Little piggies
67 Nat Turner's rebels
68 Not even

Down

1 Torah readers
2 Exotic pet
3 Vintner Paul
4 Acted nervously
5 Baseball stat
6 Neither go-with
7 South African Peace Nobelist
8 Computer owners
9 Sentence stopper
10 Crunch targets
11 Pepsi rival
12 Swaps
13 Shark's weapon?
18 Take on
22 Sister ___ ("We Are Family" singers)
25 "___ go bragh!"
26 Ladder section
28 Copycat

31 Taxi equipment
33 Unavailable, as a position
35 Most exhausted
36 Vouch for
37 Where loafers hang out?
38 Alternative to high water
39 Olfactory stimulus
40 Boy, in Bogotá
44 Checks (out)
46 Street urchin
47 Altogether
48 Caught
49 Empty-___ (having gained nothing)
51 Court proceeding
53 Program parts
56 Southwest sight
59 Scrabble 3-pointers
61 Show off on one's Harley
62 Actor's aid

43

The Great Invisible

Across

1 Spoiled kid
5 Long-term spy
9 Bird with a harsh voice
14 "I could ___ horse!"
15 Computer brand
16 It's about half the size of pica type
17 Invisible instrument
19 Social division in India
20 Lab sample
21 State whose capital is Bismarck: abbr.
22 "The Cosby Show" star Phylicia ___
23 King Kong, for one
24 Stunted ends
25 Invisible company
33 Philosopher Kierkegaard
34 Chef's hat
35 The, to Germans
36 Salt Lake City college team
37 Part of M.O.
38 Bog down
39 Deeply paradoxical
40 "Anger Management" actress Marisa
41 Hourglass contents
42 Invisible beams
45 Business big shot
46 ___ out (stretch your credit card limit)
47 Unemotional
50 Like some late-night TV
52 Face part
55 Pepe ___ (TV skunk)
56 Invisible prop
58 Battle venue
59 Hand lotion additive
60 Bakery need
61 Flavored like some toothpaste
62 Noun-making suffix
63 Waiting room call

Down

1 Bracelet piece
2 Drought need
3 Razor name
4 Kid's game requiring no equipment
5 First, as a voyage
6 Prefix meaning eight
7 Tire problem
8 Make a mistake
9 Like Edgar Allan Poe stories
10 Andre of tennis
11 ATM output
12 Encouraging preceder of "boy" or "girl"
13 Garden hassle
18 Take off a diaper, e.g.
22 Singer Wainwright
23 Gets better, like wine
24 Syrup that'll knock you out
25 Trooper automaker
26 Inn
27 "___ we all?"
28 ___ bomb
29 Place to see clowns get trampled
30 Minneapolis suburb
31 Big-brained
32 Ball wear
37 Got out of town
38 Groucho or Harpo
40 Strip of land used before takeoff
41 Remains
43 Give in
44 Pageant hosts
47 Type of poetry gathering
48 Garr of "Young Frankenstein"
49 Ready for business
50 Agitate
51 Cookie name that's famous
52 "By ___!" (old exclamation of surprise)
53 High point
54 Departed
56 Guy
57 Director Howard

Elementary Beginnings

Across

1 Lucy's hubby
5 Raw seafood snack
10 After-shower application
14 Original sin site
15 "The Cherry Orchard" playwright Chekhov
16 Length X width
17 Hollywood's nickname
19 Marty Feldman's "Young Frankenstein" role
20 Paula who sang "Straight Up"
21 Approval, in Amiens
22 Companionless
23 Church official
25 Nonstick stuff
27 Excommunication candidate
29 Haifa's land
32 Did a cobbling job
35 Sport for the stout
36 Funny Stewart
39 Picket-line participant
41 Groom's garb
42 Perlman of "Cheers"
44 Surround
46 Oklahoman
48 Dinnerware washer
52 Later
55 Layers
56 Beast of burden
58 Architect I. M. ___
60 Bridge seats
61 Tiny bit
62 Taking charge
64 Ardor
65 One-way sign symbol
66 Model Macpherson
67 With competence
68 Crystal of country music
69 Twosome

Down

1 Disengage
2 Like many mushrooms
3 Word in an Elvis title
4 Underwriter
5 Mineo of movies
6 Second word of the golden rule
7 Thickset
8 Funnyman Mandel
9 Bed-and-breakfast
10 Clothes pros
11 Golden Fleece seeker
12 Russian revolutionary Trotsky
13 Part of TLC
18 Authority exercising groups
22 Michaels and Yankovic
24 Water reservoir
26 "Semper ___" (Marine's motto)
28 It grows in ears
30 Ostrich look-alike
31 Bagel topper
33 Tyler of "The Incredible Hulk"
34 ___ out a win
36 PSAT takers
37 Exclamation of surprise
38 Of newborns
40 Roll-call list
43 Deviation from the norm
45 Put into words
47 Greek vowel
49 How bad decisions may be made
50 Hun honcho
51 Caught one's breath
53 "Carmen," for one
54 Fatigued
56 Ms. Minnelli
57 Leopold's partner in crime
59 Golden calf, e.g.
62 Jet ___
63 Farm female

Can We Talk?

Across

1. Mushroom cloud maker, briefly
6. Rush letters
10. "Hey, over here!"
14. African language
15. "___ Buy Me Love"
16. Ancient road to Rome
17. "Bah humbug!"?
19. Fish-eating eagle
20. Sun. speech
21. Bunch of bulls
22. IRA-establishing legislation
23. Grunts from a server?
26. Wore thin
29. Make mushy
30. Black, to bards
31. Sales pitch
33. Nebraska native
36. Queens English?
40. "Told ya so!"
41. Okay, in a way
42. Spitting sound, in comics
43. Debate topic
45. Latin carol opener
47. Olive bottler's shoptalk?
51. Nash of note
52. Claim on property
53. "Welcome" site?
56. Skin softener
57. Blather from Vanna?
60. Hooded garment
61. Castro's country
62. Lint trap?
63. Give an edge to
64. Knee neighbor
65. Family car

Down

1. Early lessons
2. In the buff
3. ___ about (roughly)
4. Everest and McKinley
5. 4 pecks
6. Squirrel's prize
7. New York restaurateur
8. What comes between partners?
9. NBA tallies
10. Bore through
11. Hitters' misses
12. Get a gut feeling
13. Halloween option
18. Make, as one's way
22. Viscounts' superiors
23. Chinese secret society
24. Drives for pleasure
25. Bemoaned
26. Some toothpastes
27. One of the winds
28. "Lighten up!"
31. Catch a break?
32. Loudspeakers, briefly
34. Threaded metal fastener
35. Garfield's sidekick
37. "A Doll's House" playwright
38. Sling mud at
39. Phone abbr.
44. Brosnan TV role
45. Suit to ___
46. Menace of comics
47. Hunt illegally
48. Domed home
49. Suspect's story
50. Tennessee gridder
53. Brainstorm generator
54. Singapore setting
55. Student driver, typically
57. Johns in Britain (abbr.)
58. "Come again?"
59. Married or single

Celtic Crosses

Across

1 Hazzard County police officer
7 Shocked sound
11 Two below XL
14 Animal prized for its wool
15 Possessing power
16 Blvd. cousin
17 Toast-and-cheese dish
19 "___ the season..."
20 Prepares a fishing line
21 It may be floated
22 Marquis de ___
23 Semicircles
24 Every breath you take
25 Minnesotan
27 Hard liquor choice
28 Green reporter
29 Old-fashioned contraction
30 Verify, IRS-style
32 New Hampshire-born president
33 Certain Monopoly token
37 Participates in a summer camp activity
38 Banks of baseball
39 Signs of the future
40 Newspaper people, for short
41 Dollop
44 Makes good on one's debts
46 They hook up IVs
47 Location
48 Territory
49 Dante's "Divine Comedy," for instance
51 Some artists' studios
52 Night before
53 Drink topped with whipped cream
55 "Just a ___" ("hold on")
56 Impressive basketball feat
57 Agatha Christie title word
58 Prior to, in poems
59 Iowa State University's town
60 Razor targets

Down

1 One place for seafood
2 Owner of an infamous cow
3 Do some genetic engineering
4 Fills roles
5 Newspaper publisher Adolph
6 Musical taste
7 "Gigi" actress Eva
8 "Waterloo" singers
9 Injured arm's support
10 Garfield or Marmaduke
11 Infamous Dutch spy
12 Exhibit A, maybe
13 Person who's way off-base?
18 Courtroom defenses
22 Ball
24 Autobahn vehicles
26 Brother and husband of Isis
28 Affectedly adorable
30 Hard on the ear, maybe
31 Most common English word
32 Awaits judgement
33 "Raging Bull" director Martin
34 Visited
35 Like some bathing suits
36 Warfare variety
41 Be unlike
42 Show up for
43 Harasses
45 Antitoxin
46 Puts on the line
47 Bulgaria's capital
50 Needle source
51 Possibly apocryphal history
53 Journalist Tarbell
54 Kernel's home

A Place for Everything

Across

1 Troupe group
7 Cuts off
11 Taste test
14 "Minute Waltz" composer
15 Shootin' ___
16 Santa's trailer, perhaps
17 Beethoven's Third
18 Greens keeper
20 Grade schooler's recommendation, part 1
22 QB's undoing
23 At bat stat
24 "Pride and Prejudice" author
26 Condo cousin
28 Rob of "Silk Stalkings"
31 Austin-to-Houston dir.
32 Bewildered
34 Brain or blind follower
36 Grade schooler's recommendation, part 2
38 Dalai Lama's city
40 Stunk up the place
41 Slump
42 "La Traviata" composer
43 Individually
47 Disloyal
50 Get off the fence
52 Cote quote
53 Grade schooler's recommendation, part 3
57 Devilish
58 "1984" author
59 "Losing My Religion" band
60 James Mason's 1954 captain
61 Tearjerker, in Tewkesbury
62 Constitution letters
63 Adam's apple location
64 Trojan War sage

Down

1 Vinegary
2 Logical beginning
3 Liked immediately
4 Andy Taylor's kid
5 Tater tool
6 Crisp veggie
7 "How to Murder Your Wife" star Virna
8 Like some history
9 Lively Bohemian dances
10 Major screw-up
11 1942 Hitchcock thriller
12 All fouled up
13 Hole goal
19 Salk and Pepper: abbr.
21 Fail to explode
25 Surfing site
27 Apt name for a pope?
29 Printer powder
30 Spurred
33 Pistol-packing PAC
34 Pavlova's turning point?
35 Uncouth
36 Take-down artists, perhaps
37 Flee
38 Baton Rouge sch.
39 Crying needs
42 Like some threats
44 Endure without protest
45 "Gangsta's Paradise" Grammy-winner
46 It's uproariously funny
48 Lee-side defender
49 Barely ahead
51 Babe Ruth's number
54 Croce's "___ in a Bottle"
55 PC pic
56 Ladies of the field
57 "All the King's Men" star Joanne

M-Bedded

Across

1 Desire
5 Nights before
9 Former Israeli prime minister ____ Meir
14 Singer Collins
15 Fashion
16 Zodiac ram
17 "Harry Potter" garb
18 Kid's boo-boo
19 Pileggi of "The X-Files"
20 Teacher of medieval battles?
23 "Without further ____..."
24 Sermon subj.
25 "Uncle Tom's Cabin" villain Simon ____
27 "Amazing" magician famous for debunking
29 Words on a Renault
32 iPhone program
33 Santa ___, Calif.
35 Cassette tape successors
36 Milo's buddy, in a film
37 Fill up with a painter's outfit?
41 Arm bone
42 Actor Holbrook
43 Deaf person's communication: abbr.
44 "___ want a hula hoop..."
45 Vegas area, with "The"
47 Rock in Australia
51 Quarterback legend Dan
53 Olympics chant
55 Baby goat sound
56 Words uttered upon switching brands of jelly?
60 Seller's counterpart
61 Engrossed
62 They're of miner concern
63 April Fool's day joke
64 Ending for "teen"
65 Give the eye
66 Tennis great Monica
67 Bizarre art style
68 Pianos have 88

Down

1 Commotion
2 Beach Boys hit "Help Me, ___"
3 Josh or Debbie
4 K-6 schooling, for short
5 Play to the back crowd
6 "The Partly Cloudy Patriot" author Sarah
7 Get to work on "Time"?
8 Tarot cards reader, for one
9 Like venison, compared to beef
10 Letter-shaped mechanical part
11 Authors and such
12 Like long-abandoned buildings
13 Cigar remnant
21 Lena's role on "Alias"
22 State whose motto is "North to the future"
26 Some music purchases, for short
28 Information
30 Bacterial infection...
31 ...and an org. that monitors it
34 Actor Kutcher
36 Just
37 "Business or ___?"
38 Michelin rival
39 Make a dent
40 Singer Hayes or physicist Newton
41 "Lemme think..."
45 Underwater toons of the 1980s
46 Worked on an oil rig
48 Come out
49 Hardly, if ever
50 Mouths off
52 "Mr. Belvedere" mom ___ Graff
54 Kama ___
57 Alum
58 Long story
59 Nutball
60 Way to measure pulse rates: abbr.

Call it Quits

Across

1 Sportscaster Bob
7 Third degrees, usually
11 PB&J alternative
14 Secret stuff
15 Harvest
16 The old college cry
17 "Coal Miner's Daughter" Oscar-winner Sissy
18 Remedy
20 Call it quits like a maid?
22 Turned tail
23 ___ Z (you name it)
24 "Just you wait, ___ 'iggins..."
25 Almost out of gas
29 Assault rifle
32 Mars or Milky Way unit
33 Without a ___ (broke)
34 Hand-me-down
35 Brighton brew
36 Call it quits like an electrician?
39 "Where ___?"
41 Beginning
42 A pop
43 Sib.
44 Hit head-on
45 "10" actress
49 Film fragment
51 Blue bird
53 U2 producer Brian
54 Call it quits like a cowboy?
60 Attractive
61 High-muck-a-muck
62 "___ Bravo" (John Wayne film)
63 Lewd look
64 State without proof
65 Craving
66 Bitsy beginning
67 Cornhusker rival

Down

1 Big man in Havana
2 Annie of the comics, for one
3 Gaming guru John
4 Tampico treat
5 Freshly
6 Pseudonym of H. H. Munro
7 Whitney's partner in aviation
8 Fowl facility
9 Desert fruit
10 Broiler accessory
11 The noontime sack of an officeworker?
12 Pigskin pitchout
13 Vega's constellation
19 Mommie deer
21 Equine vote?
26 East Lansing sch.
27 Arctic
28 Oklahoma oil center
30 Herbert Marx
31 Loafed
34 Channels 14 and up
36 After-the-whistle contact
37 "It's Not Unusual" singer
38 Mary of "Where Eagles Dare"
39 Robin Hood's skill
40 "Working Girl" Griffith
45 "See ya"
46 Deli sandwich
47 Make one's blood boil
48 Legit
50 Links letters
52 Irritated
55 Wrinkly tangelo with a bad name
56 Painter Mondrian
57 Jacuzzis
58 Unaided
59 Prince Charles's game

Look Who's Here!

Across

1 Two bells, at sea
6 Football's Papa Bear
11 Thought waves
14 Visionary?
15 Plain People
16 Bud's comic buddy
17 Euro casualty
18 Bonkers
19 Word of disagreement
20 Roseanne or Rosie
23 Bogart's topper
26 Ripped off
27 Lance of justice
28 Compassionate letters
30 Lateral leader
31 Eager eater
35 Gym tallies
39 Pooh goo
40 Word that's conferred
41 Software mailing, perhaps
42 Broken in
43 Farm worker
45 Long-jawed swimmer
48 Greek F
49 Long swimmer
50 Cookie cookery
55 Surrounded by
57 "The Herring Net" painter
59 Toil and trouble
60 Classic theater
61 Java selection
65 Like a crescent moon
66 Marshall of "Awakenings"
67 Harebrained
68 Buffoon
69 Elizabethan earl
70 Like Dilbert

Down

1 "Pow!" response
2 "All Things Considered" network
3 Hellenic vowel
4 Patchy pony
5 Fields adversary Charlie
6 Coil of yarn
7 Imperative
8 Kind of print
9 Pigeonhole
10 Lavish bestowal
11 Nudge
12 WWI director of all US navy bands
13 Silly stuff
21 "Mission: Impossible" theme composer Schifrin
22 Coiffure
23 Light triangular scarf
24 Group character
25 Lorna of Exmoor
29 Either horn of a crescent moon
32 Crams
33 It's nothing
34 Plunge
36 Screwed up
37 Masquerades
38 Get the lead out?
41 Piped up
44 "Pow!"
46 Inclined
47 19th-century British diamond king
50 Swahili sahib
51 Staffers
52 Recognizes
53 Buck of "Hee Haw"
54 Get on the horn
56 Castle of the turkey trot
58 Black quartz
62 Road runner
63 Partners' go-between
64 Whimsical

GR-R!

Across

1 "Four Weddings and a Funeral" actor Grant
5 "Rhyme Pays" rapper
9 When you get it, you've had it
14 Eggshell
15 Enveloping glow
16 Beat around the bush
17 "More's the pity"
18 Smaller numbers for larger numbers
20 Became depleted
22 Broadway comedy of 1964
23 Random number generator
24 "Holy moly!"
26 Like flan
30 "The Turn of the ___"
32 Parking place for parkas
34 Sounds of serendipity
35 Fundamental
37 Strike quickly
38 Strike yield
39 Follow a pattern?
40 Carrier letters
41 He's always around for the last harvest
44 Naysayer
45 Legendary city of gold
46 Conjunction of choice
47 Part of CBS
48 Label A or B, e.g.
50 Norman's norm
51 Unharden the garden, in a way
53 William Tell, for one
57 Creedence Clearwater Revival hit of 1969
61 Norwegian royal name
62 ___ Jam
63 The first Harrah's was here
64 A ___ bagatelle
65 Champing at the bit
66 "The Seven Lively ___" (Gilbert Seldes)
67 River of Flanders

Down

1 Get the word
2 "Daily Bruin" publisher
3 Home of the Gerald R. Ford Museum
4 Brazen wenches
5 Verdi villain
6 Pungent Indian dish
7 Madonna album of '92
8 Greek cross
9 Like some traffic
10 Brake one's boat
11 Erie hrs.
12 Mature
13 Makes one's mark
19 Crowd favorite
21 Cut down
25 Search party
27 Ballpark guidelines
28 Bothers
29 Private aye?
30 Three-stripers
31 Cliff Robertson's 1968 Oscar role
33 Credit-tracking corp.
35 Almost equal to Ali?
36 Champing at the bit
38 "Bobby Hockey"
42 Hen and Goose
43 Hollow muffin-shaped pastry
44 "___ of a Murder"
46 Truth in Lending no.
49 Olympic competition
52 Sans sibs
54 Piccadilly Circus statue
55 Like a day in June?
56 Last word of the 23rd Psalm
57 Dean's list stat.
58 Cable chihuahua
59 Have a little lamb
60 Sinn Féin's gp.

All Joked Up

Across

1 What some pools consist of
5 Thick liqueur
10 Fleshy fruit
14 A turn and a half on the ice
15 Screw thread, for example
16 Diabolical
17 Final Four letters
18 Liqueur flavoring
19 Diminished by
20 What comedians use to keep others from stealing their jokes?
23 Flamenco cry
24 "Dream ___" (1959 Bobby Darin hit)
25 "I forgive you"
27 "Peter Pan" pooch
28 It may be a bust
29 Helpless with laughter
32 Big horn
35 Dough dispenser
36 Like NBC, before Seinfeld quit?
40 Tsp. or tbsp.
41 Comics canine
42 War of 1812 treaty site
43 Infamous insider Ivan
46 1994 Jodie Foster film
48 Sour, cold rice dish
49 Junipero Serra, for one
51 Exhilarated state
54 Heckler's directive?
57 Hazard
58 Copious
59 One of Chekhov's "Three Sisters"
60 Las Vegas opener
61 Secluded spots
62 Pink or pillow follower
63 Working stiff
64 Thus far
65 Socks

Down

1 "Oh! Susanna" instrument
2 Get straight A's
3 Tantalize
4 Blind strip
5 Across-Styx boatman
6 Like new
7 Favored few
8 Moneygrubber
9 Biz boss
10 Fronton missile
11 Hyperbolize
12 Lose, as an opportunity
13 U.S. Open champ of '94 and '97
21 Primary strategy
22 Palindromic bird
26 Not the least blowzy
27 Medical research agcy.
28 When tripled, a McCartney/ Jackson chart-topper
29 Clears the deck
30 It may be a stretch
31 Corroborates, in court
33 William Tell's canton
34 "I'm Sorry" singer
37 Tickled-pinkness
38 Gave the twice-over
39 Orr org.
44 Rattled
45 All in the family
47 Frank's comics colleague
49 Cougars
50 Put on
51 Shaky dessert choice
52 Umbrella
53 Concord or Catawba
55 Baby's favorite art movement?
56 Kid around
57 Criminal charge

Concealed Revolvers

Across

1 Left the bed
6 Castle protection
10 Ivan the Terrible, for one
14 Songstress Baker
15 Turkey, Kyrgyzstan, and so on
16 Loathe
17 Gets penalized, board-game style
19 "Or ___!" (threat ender)
20 Emulate William Hurt
21 ___ the issue (hemmed and hawed)
23 Cool eyewear
26 Kitchen scents
27 Fought over honor, maybe
28 Mother ___ (Nobel Peace Prize winner)
30 Freshly
31 "Shane" star Alan
32 "___ Brockovich"
35 Driveway stuff
36 In the middle of
39 Not to be trusted
40 Crafts go-with
42 Push
43 Group characteristics
45 Singer Don
47 Show sorrow
48 School symbol
50 Morgue sight
51 Actor Banderas
53 "One Day ___ Time"
54 Part of, as a plot
55 The ruling class
61 Einstein's strength
62 Michigan or Ontario
63 Like many Poe stories
64 Doesn't fold
65 At any time
66 Threw dough around

Down

1 Lass
2 Lennon's lady
3 "___ the season..."
4 Indian tribe for whom a state is named
5 Rose Bowl site
6 Dillon and Damon
7 Columbus sch.
8 Puts on the tube
9 Big beer mugs
10 #1 song for Bette Midler
11 Much of Louisiana's landscape
12 Befuddled
13 Clarinet player's needs
18 Didn't allow a return
22 Wrath
23 Coffee additive
24 Home, metaphorically
25 Son-in-law of Mohammed
27 Disk information
28 Like some fruit
29 Little advantage
31 Oral history
33 "___ Lucy"
34 Rival for AMEX or NASDAQ
37 Ten or fifteen, to five
38 Garden overlooks
41 More food
44 Money for waiting?
46 "Smoking or ___?"
47 BASIC command
48 Injures
49 Punjab's musical
50 Provide the hors d'oeuvres for
52 One of five Norwegian kings
56 Hawaiian instrument, for short
57 Sales ___ (company agent)
58 "___ you kidding?!"
59 Food container
60 Gelatinize

Sixties, Schmixties

Across

1 Opens the toothpaste tube
7 FedEx rival
11 Mischief maker
14 "You know how ___ can be" (Beatles line)
15 Poet, in Old England (hidden in MICROSCOPE)
16 Prefix for conservative
17 Elmore Leonard novel about a former '60s radical
19 Touch lightly on the water
20 Extreme anger
21 Govern
22 Rose of baseball or Sampras of tennis
23 Give a ton of affection to, with "on"
24 Like George Carlin's weatherman character, Al Sleet
26 Basic dance
28 Fix one's shoelaces
29 Pre-1991 political abbr.
30 ___ Nui (Easter Island)
32 Gives to the church
33 Woodstock figure who lent his name to a Ben & Jerry's flavor
35 Words of wisdom
38 Painter Magritte
39 Jerry Lewis's telethon org.
42 Group of lions
43 Absolutely positive
45 Like many a '60s gathering
49 Raggedy ___ doll
50 Les États-___
51 Famous shortstop's nickname
52 Garbage hauler
53 Old-school comic ___ Caesar
54 Peaceful chant of the '60s
57 New U.S. resident's course
58 It may be spliced
59 Mexican food served in a husk
60 Not an extrovert
61 Hershey toffee bar
62 Tough to comb

Down

1 VHF's counterpart
2 Becomes less wide
3 Artist
4 Old sayings
5 ___'s Peak (Colorado mountain)
6 Pig's place
7 Deplete
8 Shampoo target
9 Slammer
10 CIA agent
11 Comprehensive
12 British dish
13 Fast-food chain with Cajun cuisine
18 Like some faucets
22 Devoutness
23 Some linemen, in football: abbr.
24 Throw with might
25 Person behind the wheel
27 Funny Ullman
31 Farmer's area of study: abbr.
32 Supreme Court Chief Justice, 1836-64
33 Double-___ (big mobile homes)
34 Start to lose hair
35 Highest marks
36 Slow, like a worker
37 How some remember dreams
39 1920 Preakness winner
40 Performed nicely
41 "Is it ___ wonder?"
44 City south of Seattle
46 Robotic "Doctor Who" nemesis
47 University of Maine city
48 Promise maker
52 C-___ (political channel)
54 3-pointers, in football: abbr.
55 ACLU's concerns
56 Benjamin's "Law & Order" role

Continental Divide

Across

1 City on seven hills
5 The real ___
10 Directions word
14 Peak of the peak
15 Stag
16 Pennsylvania port
17 Spanish-American poet's sonnet elements
20 Coined word?
21 Indy trouble
22 Bellicose god
23 Like 22 and 24
25 Drew in mysteries
28 Less plausible, as an excuse
32 Help with the heist
33 Shampoo oil
35 ___ Tomé and Principe (African republic)
36 Physical therapy job opportunities
39 More than -er
40 Guitarist Segovia
41 Long-term spy
42 Cut it out
44 Gives a five, maybe
45 At hand
46 Assist in a crisis, with "out"
48 Minute
51 Fabled race winner
55 Whips up some stew
58 Textbook chapter
59 Word with bumps or eggs
60 "There are more names..."
61 Vault triumphs
62 Made up one's mind
63 Degenerates

Down

1 Rub
2 October birthstone
3 Computer list
4 Gets the lode out
5 Hesitant remark
6 Santa ___
7 Pen pals?
8 ___ roll
9 "What?"
10 Benefits from an error
11 First name in humor
12 Little white lies
13 "Entertainment Tonight" alum John
18 Well-ventilated
19 O'Neill title word
23 Split to be tied?
24 Nonverbal feedback
25 Did a new parent's job
26 Lower
27 Cardinal flats
28 Oslo sight
29 "This ___ happening!"
30 Birdie beater
31 February 14 purchase
33 Revolutionary group
34 Call for some Chinese
37 Flip-chart homes
38 Early Beatles hit
43 Chesapeake Bay features
44 Comic Rudner
46 Western capital
47 Curvy
48 Blue books?
49 Lion's pride
50 In the same family tree
51 Silver gait
52 :, sometimes
53 Senator's possession
54 Sushi bar selections
56 Past
57 Dandy

56

It's Questionable

Across

 1 See 32-down
 6 JPEG alternative
 9 Health resorts
 13 Caustic
 14 Grandma
 15 Relate, as a story
 16 1993 movie starring Doctor Dre and Ed Lover
 18 Mexico's ___ Mujeres
 19 ___'wester
 20 Honolulu's island
 21 Goat food, in old cartoons
 23 Nonchalant greeting
 26 Dry Italian white wine
 28 Upper left-hand corner key
 29 Anesthetic choices
 31 1980s icon with the line "I pity the fool"
 32 Therefore
 36 "So?"
 39 Hornet's home
 40 "You've got mail" ISP
 41 Golf club carrier
 42 Olive ___ (Popeye's gal)
 43 Outward appearances
 44 Campaign slogan of 1984
 51 ___ borealis
 52 "Step right ___!"
 53 "Seeking," in personals
 56 Lackluster
 57 Query from a bored slacking worker
 60 "If all ___ fails..."
 61 Frigid or million ending
 62 They may be gray
 63 Colored, as hair
 64 RB's stat
 65 Simple question type

Down

 1 Rules of the land
 2 Toyota model
 3 Big fusses
 4 Ice: Ger.
 5 Music lover's furniture
 6 Entire range
 7 Pigs ___ blanket
 8 Better than good
 9 Bee's threat
 10 1990 Oscar winner for "Goodfellas"
 11 Poe's middle name
 12 The word on the street?
 14 Old school soda brand
 17 Holds
 22 Abbr. in company names
 24 British track star Steve
 25 Rosemary, for one
 26 Stitched
 27 Will-___-wisp
 30 Keeps clear
 31 Director Gibson
 32 With 1-across, character who married Carla on "Cheers"
 33 Formulates anew
 34 Close the gap
 35 "Bravo!" shouts
 37 Romance novelist Victoria
 38 Color commentators cover it
 42 The Who's "Love Reign ___ Me"
 44 Walked through water
 45 ___-burly
 46 Delete
 47 Dressed like judges
 48 Some garden workers
 49 Feminine suffix
 50 Greyhound vehicle
 54 Upload pictures
 55 Very, pretentiously
 58 Went into seclusion
 59 Suffix for press

Top That

Across

1 The bad cholesterol
4 Isn't in a hurry
9 Pizza topping popular throughout Europe
13 Complaint
15 Ward off
16 Architect that's also a bird
17 Coffee
18 They often live in the homes of the wealthy
20 Pizza topping popular in India
22 Carrere of "Wayne's World"
23 Campus orgs.
26 Pizza topping popular in Central America
30 Lucky
33 On ___ (how some mischief is performed)
34 Shrek and others
36 ___-Cat (winter vehicle used in "The Shining")
37 Like some car air fresheners
38 Pizza topping popular in Japan
39 Medium length
40 ___ fault (overly)
41 He made a deal with the devil
42 The land a river drains
43 ___ Court
45 Pizza topping popular in Russia
47 Chair
48 Monthly pub
49 Pizza topping popular in Sweden
56 Movable digs
59 "Windows to the soul"
61 Lily family perennial
62 She fell for Tom in "Jerry Maguire"
63 "I'm outta here!"
64 Pizza topping popular in Brazil
65 Signs of the future
66 Reject

Down

1 Pres. after JFK
2 ___ Sea (highly saline body of water)
3 Stubbs of The Four Tops
4 1994 Oscar winner Martin
5 Egg
6 South American nation
7 Once, once
8 Latin for "let it stand"
9 Guitar sounds
10 Spoon bender Geller
11 Beatty of "Deliverance"
12 Ques. counterpart
14 Plant
19 Red Sea splitter
21 Mozart's "___ kleine Nachtmusik"
24 Umbrian town for St. Francis
25 Submit, as a letter
26 Cook and Crunch: abbr.
27 Abhorrent
28 Hors d'oeuvre type
29 Hat for a chef
30 B'nai ___
31 Was winning
32 Accomplishing
35 "To Die For" director Van Sant
38 Uncle for Americans
39 Actress Ann-___
41 ___ position (protesters adopt it)
42 German beer
44 Foaming at the mouth condition
46 Parade big shots
50 Roman emperor
51 "Pardon me..."
52 Squat
53 "That's so true!"
54 Pitching great Nolan ___
55 The abominable snowman
56 AAA offering
57 ___ Miss (Southern school)
58 Feathery neckwear
60 David Sanborn's instrument

Littorally Speaking

Across

1 "Beat it!"
5 Make a break for it
9 Cold tomato mold
14 "Punch and Judy" dog
15 Grad. school
16 Corner or curb follower
17 Crazed
18 Computer capacity, for short
19 Early heat
20 Hurricane's demand?
23 "The Island of the Day Before" author
24 Florentine "Life of Christ" painter
25 Apple invader
27 "Horrors!"
28 Blubber
30 Roll-call response
31 End of "The Tempest"
34 It does a bang-up job
36 "___ Wanna Cry" (Mariah Carey #1 hit)
38 Hurricane's poetic musing, "Do I ___?"
42 Didn't pass the bar?
43 Wrigley field
44 They're picked in Hawaii
45 Pop music's ___ Lobos
46 Where Mork and Mindy honeymooned
49 Smidgens
51 Precollege, to textbook publishers
53 Pyle player Jim
55 Breathtaking beast?
58 Certain response to 38-Across?
61 Novelist Nin
62 Troop group
63 Countertenor
64 Home of Bogart's falcon?
65 In apple-pie order
66 The skull and crossbones, e.g.
67 Welcome guests
68 Alice's Restaurant patron
69 This cleu has one

Down

1 "All the world's a ___"
2 Stand-up kind of guy?
3 Since day one: Lat.
4 Kid
5 Happen to meet
6 Completely paired
7 Flash or flood follower
8 Couch potatoes' fixations
9 About
10 Glass sipper
11 Gardener's bane
12 Spellbound
13 Roger Rabbit frame
21 "Eewww, gross!"
22 Pigeon English?
26 Santa Claus and the Tooth Fairy
27 Dutch baker
29 Catcher behind the plate?
31 Discombobulate
32 Union dropouts of '61
33 In-your-face mouthings
35 Running game
37 ___ ex machina
39 Ring letters
40 On-line help, often
41 Liqueur that's Italian for "rather bitter"
47 ICU staffers
48 Hilo honcho
50 Summer setting: abbr.
52 Last Supper query
54 Big goof
55 Ocean or Wilder
56 Ready to be drawn
57 Disco phrase
59 Dumb-ox connector
60 Dagger grip
61 Doc bloc

You Can't Miss It

Across

1 Modern scandal suffix
5 "Over here!"
9 Arbor Day time
14 C&W showplace
15 Klutz's cry
16 Jostle
17 Mayberry moppet
18 Come-on
19 "Later!"
20 Basketball call
23 Guys
24 British Parliament outrage of 1765
28 Proposes
30 Pearl's mom in "The Scarlet Letter"
31 With 41-Across, the central concept in Thorstein Veblen's "The Theory of the Leisure Class"
36 Hayworth hubby ___ Khan
37 Bounders down under
38 Nile nipper
39 One of Woody's kids
40 Hems and haws
41 See 31-Across
45 Corkscrew
47 Animal fat
48 Action flick, usually
51 Cavern
55 "Dewey Defeats Truman" headline, for example
57 "Key ___"
60 Screenwriter/reviewer James
61 Out-of-this-world org.
62 It's the last word in Tours
63 Seal in the juices
64 O.T. book
65 Have the ___ on
66 Angled annexes
67 Shouts of approval

Down

1 Explode
2 Northern Spy, for one
3 Due-process process
4 Spectacle
5 Polish hero of the American Revolution
6 Give the cold shoulder
7 Puts first things first
8 It's a steal
9 Takes on
10 Graves role on "Mission: Impossible"
11 Future fry
12 What a kid'll eat, in song
13 Gamboling spot
21 Grate upon
22 Where to find Sunset Beach
25 Home-entertainment pioneer
26 Ma's instrument
27 Check for fit
29 Riffle (through)
31 Gall
32 Pizzazz
33 Private disagreement
34 Carrier letters
35 Magnum follower
39 Mason, for one
41 Unsympathetic
42 Stewpot
43 Street thugs
44 ___ Noël (Santa Claus, in France)
46 Fixed
49 Clear the boards
50 Orion's left foot
52 Smidgen
53 Puccini opera
54 Verbal grillings
56 "The Subject Was Roses" star Patricia
57 Determine who breaks, in billiards
58 Big deal
59 Carnival city

Are You an Ogre?

Across

1 Word from the Arabic for "perfume"
6 Sounds masseuses hear
9 Drug in a den
14 Frequent guest on "The Love Boat"
15 "___ hear!"
16 German beer brand
17 Poisonous
18 Shane MacGowan & bandmates
20 Dubliners may talk with them
22 Wide size
23 Calendar abbr.
24 Headstone inscription
27 It requires a code
30 Makeshift windshield cleaner
32 When mastodons roamed
35 Enjoy, as benefits
37 Hefty "The Tao of Steve" star
40 Song's beginning
42 Tic-___-toe
43 Wedding acquisition
44 Unhip
47 All there
48 Tennis rival of Monica
49 Letters after O
51 Scottish refusal
52 Rower's item
53 "I get it now!" sounds
56 Egypt and Syr., once
58 Pop star who redid "The Loco-Motion"
64 No follower of international maritime law
67 Dutch shoes
68 Deck out
69 Friend of Bob and Otto?
70 Is a good doggie
71 Actress Annie
72 Drink made from leaves
73 Davis of "Grumpy Old Men"

Down

1 When the characters are introduced
2 Norse god with iron gloves
3 Cab
4 Come up, as a subject
5 French cosmetics giant Yves ___
6 Stargazing, in college course books
7 Foil-wrapped Hostess products
8 Long-term military tactic
9 Woodwind instrument
10 Identifies
11 Hospital area, for short
12 Hawaiian instrument, for short
13 Ed.'s submissions
19 Student
21 Drop of sweat
24 Poncho kin
25 Green animal some keep as a pet
26 Little kid
27 Songlike passage
28 Comic Judy ___, self-described as "The Aphrodite of the Accordion"
29 "It doesn't ___ to me"
31 Visit
33 151, once
34 Forever and a day
36 T.A.'s boss
38 Engage in henpecking
39 Belle & Sebastian's "For the Price of ___ of Tea"
41 Not on the schedule this week
45 Cousins of the cello
46 Prefix with distant
50 ___ Mirage, Calif.
54 Part of a drum set
55 Paris's river
57 Movie parts
58 Quarterback Warner
59 Aching feelings
60 Gp. that gives out NC-17s
61 Departs
62 Fruit from Jamaica
63 In ___ (at heart)
64 Music genre
65 Prefix with meter
66 Fooled

Wash What You Say

Across

1 Insects with a 17-year cycle

8 Sets (in)

14 How many dumb things are performed

15 Red shade

16 Part 1 of a boastful quote from composer Gioachino Rossini

17 Cousin of the tilde and umlaut

18 Crushes underfoot

19 In an overly huge way

20 ____ Aviv (Israeli city)

21 Bad driving weather

22 Word before "of silence" or "of poverty"

25 Quote, part 2

30 "And later ___ the crowd thinned out..." (Bob Dylan lyric)

32 Major Calif. airport

33 "Memoirs of a ___"

34 Opera stars

36 Hooting bird

38 Make like an angry rottweiler

39 Walter who played Chekov on "Star Trek"

41 Janitor's need

43 France, once

44 Quote, part 3

47 "CSI: Miami" network

48 Attach, as a ribbon

49 Bill amt.

51 Optimist's phrase

54 Point-gainers

58 Flagstaff's state

59 End of quote

60 One that dilates

61 State home to a space camp

62 Had to have

63 More likely to give orders

Down

1 Gear parts

2 Monogram ltr.

3 Spelunker's home

4 Far from bungling

5 Distressed lady, in fairy tales

6 Rings, in biology

7 Actor Penn

8 Titanic sinker

9 Flirted, in a way

10 Getting stiff, like quills

11 Palindromic magazine

12 Computer brand

13 Word before put or tuned

15 Rake over the coals

21 They melt in winter

22 Russian drink

23 Vegetable that makes you cry

24 Said hi to the cameras

26 Tabloid headline word

27 Figuring Newton

28 Garden growth

29 Starbucks sizes

31 Clean

35 Rubber-like compound

37 "Thanks a ___!"

40 Gathered, as information

42 Flute cousin

45 Submarine machine

46 Mr. Edison

50 Bait shop stock

51 Show boredom

52 One of the Great Lakes

53 Team

54 Wild guess

55 Morales of "La Bamba"

56 Icy frost

57 It may show after stitches

Tool Shed

Across

1 Prison
5 One of the four seasons: abbr.
8 Backup operation
13 Emasculate
15 Sorority letter
16 War hero Murphy
17 From Japan, old-style
19 Picture
20 Company that merged with Bell Atlantic
21 Came to one's senses
23 Don who pitched the only perfect World Series game
25 Every bit
26 Fishing tools
27 Late director ___ Kazan
28 "Now it makes sense!"
30 Hired thugs
32 Peevish
35 Poli ___ (college major)
38 "It should be familiar from here"
41 Submissions to eds.
42 Came up
43 Support for the arts?
44 Letters on beer bottles
45 Funnyman ___ Laurel
46 Sonny's former partner
49 Electric fish
52 Hold together
54 Loose garment featured in the "U Can't Touch This" video
57 Notes that follow dos
58 Leafy shelter
59 Causes the washer to rattle
61 "...___ man with seven wives..."
62 Signed like an illiterate
63 When a signal is given
64 Precursor to Windows
65 More than mos.
66 Biol. energy sources

Down

1 Playground bars
2 "Gentlemen Prefer Blondes" novelist
3 Domineering
4 Cat's place for petting
5 More than a mere soup
6 Fusilli or farfalle
7 Mercedes of "The Fisher King"
8 Jack and Jill's item
9 Chevy model
10 Common observation
11 From dusk until dawn
12 Red vegetables
14 Neighbor of the mouth
18 Palindromic woman's name
22 Make happy
24 Dropped like an anchor
29 Mr. ___ (Dr. Jekyll's counterpart)
31 Unforeseen trouble
32 Couple
33 Alien life forms
34 That ship
35 Movie where Whoopi Goldberg played a nun
36 Explained fully
37 They may be faked to skip work
39 Talk to the waiter
40 Diaper woe
44 Detective played by Peter Lorre
46 "My Name is Asher Lev" writer Potok
47 In ___ way (in danger)
48 Put (inside)
50 Adhesive component
51 Tennis great Rod ___
52 Mid.
53 Capital of Norway
55 Notable times
56 Beatty and Flanders
60 ___ whim (without forethought)

Central Bark

Across

1 Bench or post follower
5 1995 earthquake city
9 Woody Allen's pseudo-documentary set in the 1920s
14 Lotion lily
15 In full flower
16 Conjure up
17 ___ seats (top row)
19 Slanted surface
20 It may be breathing down your neck
22 Couric's cohost
23 Jane of fiction
24 1974 John Wayne cop flick
27 Parapsychology letters
28 Winter hrs. in Wichita
30 Diner sign
33 Buttinsky
35 Pitched in
36 Stand-up guy
40 Bowery bums
41 Supermodel Lanzoni
42 One from column A and one from column B
45 "Bugs"
46 Mantras
49 Calypso kin
50 "Blondie" tyke
52 "West Side Story" song
54 The three bears, for one
58 Like Sidney Lumet's 12 men
60 Either Hoffa, for a time
61 Hägar the Horrible's honey
62 Lilliputian
63 Pizzazz
64 "Skittle Players" artist Jan
65 "Macbeth" trio
66 Auto making a comeback?

Down

1 It's a wrap
2 Hellos for haoles
3 Was revolting
4 Nancy Drew's creator
5 Coke nut
6 Gilbert and Sullivan production
7 Muscular
8 Hang in there
9 Indian ox
10 Loving and lasting leader
11 Beatles chart-topper of '64
12 Head Turner, until the mid-70s
13 Come together
18 Lullaby
21 Leaves for a drink from a bag?
25 All hands on deck
26 End-of-proof letters
29 Where "Wayne's World" began, for short
31 Good luck charm
32 The Big Island's biggest city
33 "Son of Frankenstein" shepherd
34 Central bark
36 Curling place
37 Involve in intrigue
38 Leaning toward
39 "Charlotte's Web" monogram
40 "Vampire in Brooklyn" director Craven
43 Elder elver
44 Olivier/Caine mystery of '73
46 Baseball bird
47 "(There's) No Gettin' Over Me" singer Ronnie
48 Declines
51 Craze
53 Color in "America the Beautiful"
55 Compulsion
56 Printer's blue
57 Vaudeville's Seven Little ___
58 Patient sounds
59 The bottom line

Required Reading

Across

1 Engrossed
5 Alternative to nothing
8 It's one-and-a-half calories
14 Burmese sound
15 Author Edgar Allan ___
16 Cheese usually grated
17 Dr. Seuss book everyone read at age 5
20 It may be tacked on
21 Like most dorms
22 Basmati, e.g.
23 Chicken ___ King
25 One type of nest egg
27 Suffix meaning "recipients of an action"
29 Padre's brother
30 Mark Twain book everyone read at age 10
34 Butter alternative
35 Tyler of "The Lord of the Rings"
36 ___-cone (fair cooler)
37 Topsy-___
39 Not positive: abbr.
41 Muscle problem
45 Ending for super
47 "Automatic for the People" band
49 Hollywood "goodbye"
50 Salinger book everyone read at age 15 (with "The")
55 ___Kosh B'Gosh (clothing brand)
56 Petrarch work
57 Actress Longoria
58 Sean Penn title role of 2001
59 Other, to Ortega
61 Fashion's Christian ___
63 Move like a toad
65 Ayn Rand book everyone read at age 20
70 Modern notes
71 "___ be an honor!"
72 Campbell of "Scream 3"
73 Snare drum noise
74 Place for a voyage
75 Garfield's dog pal

Down

1 D&D, for one
2 Sound-related prefix
3 Introductory person
4 Elm or oak
5 Baboon's cousin
6 Lincoln was born in one
7 Brick toy for kids
8 Stock exchange workers
9 Charged particle
10 Mil. head honcho
11 Gauguin's Pacific island
12 Aleve alternative
13 "Now, seriously!"
18 Playwright Simon
19 Person with the vision
23 "Cat on ___ Tin Roof"
24 "Little" comic strip character
26 Bahaism, for one: abbr.
28 Lip ___
31 Ron on whom "Born on the Fourth of July" was based
32 "The first time ___ saw your face..."
33 Leave choiceless
38 Start of a pirate's cry
40 Come up with
42 Mach 1, e.g.
43 Angelou or Lin
44 Robert Frost work
46 Feature of southwestern bike trails
48 Cable channel with "The Real World"
50 "The Dukes of Hazzard" garage owner
51 Inhaler's target
52 It may be empty
53 Horse rider's handful
54 1980s scandal figure Jessica
60 "What do you make ___?"
62 Redding of soul
64 "Horrors!"
66 Ending for pay or cup
67 Muckraking journalist Tarbell
68 Quicktime file extension
69 Ruby of "The Stand"

Check, Please!

Across

1 Jar contents in a coffeehouse
5 Everest and Fuji, e.g.
8 Clinton's successor, casually
13 Quatrain rhyme scheme, sometimes
14 "What a relief!"
15 Lack of acknowledgement
16 Stitched (together)
17 They're new to the beat
19 1989 Best Actress winner
21 Turn, as a chair
22 Coat of arms symbol
24 Lamb's sound
25 Gumbo vegetable
29 Spiral-shaped pasta
31 Corporal punishment inflictor
32 Aberdeen resident
34 What Jim Morrison claimed he was, in song
37 "Raiders of the Lost ___"
38 European peak
39 Tex-___ cuisine
40 Earth: pref.
41 Rat Packer in the original "Ocean's Eleven"
44 "What time?"
45 Farmer's expanse
46 Newsgroup source
48 Hug's accompaniment
49 A good time
51 Gave a wanton look
54 Common food, or its color
57 Backbone
58 One place to get a cone
62 "American ___"
63 Makes amends
64 Genetic messenger
65 Dickens heroine Little ___
66 Hands, to Diego
67 Wd. in Roget's Thesaurus
68 Pate de foie ___

Down

1 Sample, as soup
2 Steel girder
3 Cash sources in tight situations
4 Place for neighborhood baseball games
5 Scratch the surface?
6 Art colony of New Mexico
7 Realm covered by "Entertainment Weekly"
8 "Groove Is in the Heart" singers ___-Lite
9 Reveal
10 Unauthorized book, maybe
11 Talk nonstop
12 Michaels and Gore
15 Mariah Carey or Celine Dion
18 Sportage and Sorento maker
20 "Are we there ___?"
23 Prefix with meter or liter
26 1980s show with a talking car
27 Zellweger of "Bridget Jones's Diary"
28 Gas used in lasers
30 Little sips, as of booze
31 410
32 Pat of "Wheel of Fortune"
33 Plants related to the iris
35 "Famous" cookie guy
36 Stave off
38 Muscles in a "six-pack"
42 Type of question with a simple answer
43 Yearns (for)
44 Crying
47 Super Mario Bros. console, for short
49 Internet explanation pages
50 Palindromic Burmese prime minister
52 ___ Gay (famous airplane)
53 Some computers
55 Seedless and marble
56 "___, meeny, miney, moe..."
58 Grand Coulee, for one
59 ___ standstill
60 "Am ___ the list?"
61 Palindromic woman's name

Pop Quiz

Across

1 1994 Tommy Lee Jones flick
5 ___ facto
9 Camouflage
13 Collective-bargaining establishment
15 "An ill wind that nobody blows good"
16 Sharp erectile bristle
18 Frozen dessert chain
19 Adjective in a mall's boast
20 Secret store
23 Elbows
24 Sultana's chambers
25 "Goldengirl" Anton
27 Yodeler's range?
31 Pedigreed pooch
32 Cub with a club
33 Norwegian toast
34 Possible political title of the 1990s, perhaps
38 Like Poe's prose
39 "Beat the skins"
40 Chihuahua cheer
41 Concrete
42 Excite, as interest
44 Cockeyed
45 Pockets
47 Menacing
48 Champion
51 Aretha Franklin's "___ No Way"
53 Hodgepodge
57 Village Voice award
58 Pleased
59 USSR news agency
60 Utopia
61 60-Across fruit

Down

1 Green goal
2 Japanese Beatle?
3 Labor movements?
4 Italian bowling
5 The first Cosby show
6 Honor society letter
7 State below Arizona
8 Give access to
9 Greek eggplant dish
10 "That's ___ much"
11 Work alone
12 Iodine-rich food from the sea
14 Heart of the matter
17 Proof finale
20 Tucson's ___ Bowl
21 Renée of "The Big Parade"
22 Exposure unit?
23 Theme of this puzzle
25 Native land
26 Put to work
28 New Orleans or Chicago university
29 Pastiness
30 Dopey companion
32 Thou, to a frau
33 Dim ___
35 Muzzles
36 1990 Robert Morse Tony-winner
37 Hernando's "Huh?"
42 Juliet of "G.I. Blues"
43 Encroachment
44 End of some plays
46 Butt bit
47 Up to ___ (acceptable)
48 Pickle
49 Sunblock ingredient
50 "The Dock of the Bay" singer Redding
51 Analogous
52 Mental figures, familiarly
54 Short way to go?
55 Gam
56 Oilers' strikes, briefly

Literary Gifts

Across

1 German John
5 Beau Brummells
9 Go-between
14 Settled down
15 Where to find the ruins of Babylon
16 Jackie's predecessor
17 Roman historian
18 Seesaw sitter of verse
19 Ransack
20 Hersey's story of the WWII American occupation of a small Italian town
23 "Nothing Compares 2 U" singer O'Connor
24 Baby bloomer
25 Hightailed it
28 Token takers
31 Huge flop
33 Triple ___ (orange liqueur)
36 With 42-Across, O'Neill's "Long Day's Journey Into Night" sequel
38 Persia, since 1935
40 Tears for Fears, e.g.
41 Working stiff
42 See 36-Across
47 Gunn's gun
48 Gas pump word
49 Surround
51 Down or down time
52 Birds do it
54 Turn pale
58 Faulkner's first short story published in a national magazine
62 Decision-maker in a box
64 Closing passage
65 Didn't just pass
66 Monkeyshine
67 Swamp swimmer
68 Whaler's adverb
69 Peter of "Taxi Driver"
70 In this case
71 Juno, to the Greeks

Down

1 NFL cofounder George
2 Cover story
3 Phileas Fogg portrayer
4 Couturier's concerns
5 Feudal estate
6 "___ I'm told"
7 '50s talk-show pioneer
8 Fowl entrée
9 "The Shadow" medium
10 Capital ___
11 "Where Angels Fear to Tread" author
12 Diddly-squat
13 Green launching pad
21 In ___ land (loopy)
22 Backside
26 Sound from a dwarf
27 Interminably
29 Foofaraw
30 Went ___ (turned bad)
32 Dada papa
33 "The Goodbye Girl" writer
34 Jong or Kane
35 Last-night fling
37 C or key follower
39 Grizzlies' gp.
43 Administer, as the law
44 Thickens
45 Welcome
46 Christie's "Death on the ___"
50 Super Bowl III MVP Joe
53 "Guh-ross!"
55 Specialized market
56 Unmistakable
57 "Two heads are better than one" monster?
59 Churn
60 Father's preceder, but not mother's
61 Something fishy?
62 Fast poke
63 One, to Juan

68

No Gain

Across

1 "To ___ it may concern..."
5 Drives the getaway car
10 Greek wrap
14 Indian woman's garment
15 ___ Picchu
16 2012 or 2020
17 "Hold on a sec!"
18 Earthy tone
19 Lion's hair
20 OBSERVATION, PART 1
23 Attacks
25 Desert watering holes
26 Superman's birth name
27 Leaves out
30 OBSERVATION, PART 2
35 Tennis barrier
36 H.H. ___ (Saki)
37 "Dig in!"
39 OBSERVATION, PART 3
44 Edmonton athlete
45 Lymph
46 Sandy trouble
49 47-down models
51 END OF OBSERVATION
55 Start the poker pot
56 Informed
57 Words before "old chap"
60 Conception
61 Geographical formation named for a Greek letter
62 Latin phrase for a backstabber
63 Fat for cooks
64 Lend ___ (listen)
65 Contact the host

Down

1 One way to go: abbr.
2 "I told you so!" laugh
3 Montana's state motto, which means "gold and silver" in Spanish
4 Made kitty sounds with all 5 vowels?
5 "___ Andy" (old radio show)
6 Family of composers
7 Rotunda effect
8 Drive-___ window (bank feature)
9 Gibberish-talking "SNL" character ___ Forrester (anagram of ULSE)
10 Mary Lou Retton, for one
11 "The Wild Swans at Coole" poet
12 Mountain group
13 Dunkable cookies
21 Gross-sounding fruit
22 "Methinks the lady ___ protest too much"
23 Sacred image: var.
24 "The Absinthe Drinker" painter
27 Dog's master
28 Like a swamp
29 "Was ___ harsh?"
31 Olympic runner Zatopek
32 It can be whistled
33 Whiplash preventers
34 Like many roofs
38 "Guarding ___" (Shirley MacLaine movie)
40 Proceed
41 "Mystic Pizza" actress Taylor
42 Weird, to a Scotsman
43 Indiana native
46 Very slow creature
47 Japanese automaker
48 Weasel relative
49 Biggest artery
50 Without a cloud in the sky
52 Zilch
53 Singer ___ Stefani
54 Fairy ___
58 Off-roader of sorts
59 "Uh-huh"

Looking Good

Across

1 Baseball great Carl, for short
4 Like vulgar humor
10 "The King and I" locale
14 Suffix for Japan or Taiwan
15 Slow movement, in music
16 Atahualpa, for one
17 Stylish outerwear, in the 1950s
20 Free-for-all
21 Get the Dom Perignon ready
22 Checked off
24 Exact genetic copy
28 Sit-up focus
31 Stylish grooming material, in the 1920s
36 Kiddies
38 Material best kept out of the rain
39 Name for two wives of Henry VIII
40 Pulled apart
41 Word after paper or vapor
42 Get something off your chest
43 "___ Old Cowhand from the Rio Grande"
44 Heron's cousin
45 One of the Great Lakes
46 Stylish outerwear, in the 1970s
49 To be, to Bolivians
50 Pianist Rubinstein
51 El ___ (Spanish hero)
53 Take, as a position
58 Shaker's partner
62 Stylish accessories, in the 1890s
66 Late Belgian pop star Jacques (hidden in UMBRELLA)
67 Go after violently
68 Channel for teens and twentysomethings
69 Alluring
70 All the rage
71 Palindromic dog

Down

1 Subservient response
2 "A Hard Road to Glory" author Arthur
3 Fervor
4 Rapper Prince ___ (anagram of REMAKE)
5 Bouncer's concerns
6 Capital on the Caspian Sea
7 Not "fer," in the sticks
8 Member of "The Mod Squad"
9 Karate school
10 Extended absence, maybe
11 Printer fluid
12 Pass with flying colors
13 Welcome ___
18 Harrison who played Dr. Dolittle
19 St. Louis structure
23 Cleaning crew tool
25 Manual's target audience
26 Kids' caretaker: var.
27 City in SW England
28 ___ the Hun
29 Baby ___ (person born after WWII)
30 Country singer George ___
32 Sudden upswing
33 Crying drops
34 Parting word
35 Like the Irish
37 In a romantic way
47 ___ Major (constellation)
48 Just at the right moment
52 "The Simpsons" word added to the OED
54 Little fight
55 Largest nation, once
56 ___-en-scène
57 Abba ___ of politics
59 Frequent Marlene Dietrich character
60 Phrase to a traitor
61 Say you'll be there (or won't)
62 "Survivor" network
63 Stuff in a mine-altering experience?
64 ___ Luthor (Superman's enemy)
65 Cookie jar top

From the Horse's Mouth

Across

1 Laugher's sound
5 Poisonous snake
10 Thicke of TV or Turing of mathematics
14 Worked with frosting
15 Polished
16 Six inverted
17 Amorous gaze
19 Complete
20 Huge crowds
21 Like some owls
23 They hold hands
24 Cod and May
25 Thrill
28 Some church ceremonies
31 Enjoys Twain, perhaps
32 Gandolfini or Garfield
33 "Whazzat?"
34 Pre-
35 Doesn't just sip
36 Indiana city
37 Ship's plea
38 Big name in Chicago politics
39 Aesop's lesson
40 Puts in the envelope
42 How lowlifes operate
43 Hotel offerings
44 Totals
45 It's in your blood
47 Injured, as an ankle
51 Best Picture Nominee of 1981
52 Slow rate
54 Stare
55 "The Trial" author
56 One of Seth's sons
57 ___ Tavern ("The Simpsons" locale)
58 Win every game
59 Moist and cold

Down

1 Boo's partner
2 Pain in the neck, maybe
3 End of a loaf
4 Down under city
5 Take for granted
6 Some love songs
7 Week parts
8 The night before
9 Gives new form to
10 Former Soviet president Gromyko
11 Most
12 "Breathing Lessons" novelist Tyler
13 The Beatles' "I ___ You"
18 Baltimore, Boston and Bangkok
22 Makes a choice
24 Showy on purpose
25 Blot out
26 Air component
27 Kurt Vonnegut novel
28 Hay amounts
29 Wall art
30 In a reserved manner
32 Sci-fi pioneer Verne
35 Riot-police wear
36 Talked at the back fence
38 Goner's fate
39 Ladies of the house, informally
41 Red ink entries
42 Sack cloth
44 Lee of Hollywood
45 Occasion to use a limo
46 Building-blocks name
47 Bank sight
48 Grandma
49 College course, casually
50 Dilbert's place
53 "Nope"

Going to the Dogs

Across

1 Coat with gold
5 Kid-lit elephant
10 Tabloid twosome
14 Stinky smell
15 Single-handedly
16 Pig picture
17 Just say no
18 Pastrami places
19 Past partners
20 Give in to gravity
21 Those on the cutting edge
23 Guitarist Clapton
25 Toronto-to-Ottawa dir.
26 Dirty digs
27 Get down to work, with gusto
31 Explosive letters
33 Somewhat
34 Nosh from Nabisco
36 Girl scout group
40 Signature seekers
43 What's in, in fashion
44 One of a 1492 trio
45 Holy Fr. women
46 The Divine, to da Vinci
48 "Been there" partner
50 Mule of song
53 LPs' successors
55 Medicinal measure
56 Lay-ups and slam dunks, e.g.
60 Make a collar
63 Use a beeper
64 Rather, informally
65 Zeus, to Romans
66 Similar (to)
67 "Lemon Tree" singer Lopez
68 Tag line?
69 Big top, e.g.
70 George of "Where's Poppa?"
71 Rest areas?

Down

1 Neptune and Pluto, e.g.
2 Brainchild
3 Staying power
4 Like some humor
5 Lousy liar
6 One of the Baldwins
7 Tree trunk
8 Pernod flavoring
9 Bristle at
10 "Yeah, right!"
11 Uncle Sam's income
12 Film critic Roger
13 Tangled up
21 Zadora of "Butterfly"
22 10:50, vis-à-vis 11:00
24 Like stale jokes
27 Lukas of "Witness"
28 Touch on
29 Land of Tabriz
30 Not so hot?
32 Some funds
35 "Say it ain't so!"
37 Exactly
38 Ancient theaters
39 "Hey, you!"
41 Car insurer
42 Climber's clasp
47 Rhapsodic poets
49 Canon camera
50 March honoree, familiarly
51 On one's toes
52 Gain computer access
54 Sleep soundly?
57 Cooped (up)
58 Pre-calc course
59 Sicilian smoker
61 Hot-to-trot
62 Porgy's woman
65 Short punch

I Am Here in My Car

Across

1 Wander far and wide
5 Sacred Indian text
9 Multitaskers wear many
13 Norse god
14 Blow, like a volcano
16 "Whoops!"
17 It's performed at drive-thrus in Las Vegas
20 Devoured
21 Tough time to drive
22 Daisy variety
23 Chow Fun, e.g.
25 Crusader for a national park system
26 You can pick them up at pharmacy drive-thrus
32 Color that's close to mustard
34 Theater boxes
35 Writer called "the father of the detective story"
36 Furrowed facial feature
37 "Hocus-___!"
38 Pick out of a crowd
39 H+ or OH-
40 Soy or barbecue
41 Jupiter has four large ones
42 Common amount withdrawn from a drive-thru ATM
45 Assists
46 City, lake, county, or tribe of New York
49 St. ___ Girl beer
51 Rome farewell
53 Talking-___ (admonishments)
54 The classic drive-thru purchase
57 Egyptian cross
58 Try, like food
59 Dull person
60 Game where you search for red or blue pages
61 "___ believe me?"
62 Part of MIT

Down

1 Late columnist Carl
2 Beethoven's "___ Joy"
3 Teleconferencing tool
4 It can be tight or bitter
5 Concert locations
6 Rowing machine units
7 Avoid getting hit
8 Mighty Joe Young, for one
9 Arm bones
10 "Hey, sailor!"
11 Vocal inflection
12 Far from the life of the party
15 Mime groups
18 Slacking person
19 Ways out
24 Nancy ___ (detective)
25 Michael, in Mexico
27 Rain makers
28 Boxer Marciano's first name, really
29 Those against you
30 Time for palindromes?
31 Goes down, like the sun
32 Passing remark?
33 Boast triumphantly
37 Profitable discovery that's "hit"
38 Aching
40 Steps that lead over a fence
41 "I'm a ___ my word!"
43 Zippo
44 Three sheets to the wind
47 Active people
48 Advantage
49 Small and weak
50 Big boats
51 Credit alternative
52 Enthusiastic about, as a band
54 Emeril Lagasse shout
55 Was a witness
56 Baseball stat

Keep me Posted

Across

1. Sing the praises of
5. Dentist's recommendation
10. Ingrain, as into memory
14. Prepare for a deal
15. Second-grade sequence
16. Poet Teasdale
17. Philatelist's pride
20. "...was this lousy ___"
21. Luke's teacher
22. Fire fodder
23. Dawn goddess
25. French city on the Rhone
27. Dog dodger, stereotypically
34. Cook's wear
35. Enthusiastic
36. Self-satisfied
39. Lake formed by the Hoover Dam
40. Worries
41. Pete's is often cited
42. Clinton cabinet member Federico
43. Color from the French for "unbleached"
44. Gave a hand
45. 1600 Pennsylvania Avenue, for example
48. Blood variety
50. Took control
51. Tic-tac-toe victory
52. Cold war initials
56. Andean sights
61. Exceed normal limits
64. Neighborhood
65. Golden tune
66. Ready to do business
67. Vim
68. Coin-hitting-water sounds
69. Book's body

Down

1. Way out of medal contention
2. Aardvark's lunch
3. Salt Lake City's state
4. Moore of "Disclosure"
5. Aspect
6. Summer sky sight
7. Slick
8. Prima donna's time to shine
9. Looked for damages
10. Superlative finale
11. Fitting perfectly
12. Sing sentimentally
13. Stores a shirt, perhaps
18. Primp
19. Colombian city
24. Tough to find
26. Base words?
27. Genie's home
28. Olympic weapon
29. Interchanges
30. So far
31. Turn away
32. Ceremony
33. Ave. cousins
37. Hawaiian strings, for short
38. H.S. diploma alternatives
40. Charge
44. Cause confusion
46. Landslide
47. Digs deeper
48. Hitchcock classic
49. "___ not serious!?"
53. Hit the mall
54. Hawk
55. Take another shot at
57. Tons
58. Engage in self-pity
59. Top
60. Dispatched
62. It's usually over your head
63. Tuck's go-with

P.S. I Love You!

Across

1 Bit of wit
5 Husky breaths
10 Teutonic turndown
14 Countertenor
15 Midway alternative
16 "Beetle Bailey" bulldog
17 Ollie's ally
18 Drawing room
19 Accident report?
20 Kielbasa
23 "All My Children" vixen
24 Mariner's guiding light
27 Howard of "American Graffiti"
28 Sautéed entrée usually flavored with soy sauce
32 ___ Veneto
33 Missouri river
34 Calculator feature, initially
37 First course selection
40 Despicable
41 Ex-Yankee pitcher Hideki
43 Curry or Russert
44 Picnic favorite
48 R-V hookup?
51 Chart caves
52 "Dragon's Teeth" author Sinclair
54 Seafood entrée
58 Evita's hubby
60 "The Jungle Book" wolfpack leader
61 Obsessed with
62 Bikini, for one
63 Cool, lustrous fabric
64 Comic vignette
65 Really ripe
66 Satyrs' stares
67 Bits of wit

Down

1 "Harlem Light" artist Johns
2 Corrida quarry
3 He exiled Trotsky
4 Elixir
5 Luxurious
6 Cries of surprise
7 Simba's love, in "The Lion King"
8 Road company
9 Alarm component
10 Nutty treats
11 Heavenly
12 Lance of the bench
13 Yokohama drama
21 Easy mark
22 "Stay of Execution" author Stewart
25 Othello's nemesis
26 Distort
29 "The Three Faces of ___"
30 Zadora of "Hairspray"
31 Elbows on the table?
34 Smackers
35 Snip a snap
36 Tree of the desert
37 Lodge
38 Crude stuff
39 Thurman of "Batman and Robin"
42 Poppycock
45 Standing by
46 It's just north of Chicago
47 Word from Snerd
48 Drunk as a skunk
49 Small songbird
50 Prepares to transplant
53 Light bender
55 Russo of "Get Shorty"
56 Red or Cardinal, for short
57 Without
58 Dublin dance
59 "La Femme Nikita" network

I'm a Soul Man

Across

1 Strikebreaker
5 Of renown
10 Loretta of "M*A*S*H"
14 Sport played on horseback
15 Architect ___ Aalto
16 Drive-___ window
17 Wacky rocker who sported a soul patch
19 Horse pattern
20 "Me Talk Pretty One Day" humorist David
21 Musical with Olivia Newton-John
23 One of the Bobbsey twins
24 Summer camp watercraft
26 Jazz legend who sported a soul patch
32 Opera songs
33 Prefix meaning "seven"
34 Boxing match div.
36 Bites, like a puppy
37 Church features, sometimes
38 Right-hand man
39 Oxlike beast
40 Part of a healthy diet
41 Type of salts used on feet
42 Olympic skater who sports a soul patch
45 Raymond and Aaron
46 Young ___ (little tykes)
47 Ingredient in some shampoos
50 Speak haltingly
54 Actor Morales of "NYPD Blue"
55 Catcher who sports a soul patch
58 Shade trees
59 Kitchenaid competitor
60 Baseball field cover
61 Washington or Denver newspaper
62 Like beach towels
63 Times of the past

Down

1 Nos. on sunscreen bottles
2 Apple center
3 "When I was ___..."
4 They pay off big time
5 Disturbing one's composure
6 "Woe is me!"
7 Sports award, for short
8 "The Raven" monogram
9 Operations for catching crooks
10 Meryl who spoke the line "a dingo ate my baby"
11 Horse-stopping shout
12 401(k) relatives
13 Song
18 Infamous London mobsters
22 Parks of the civil rights movement
24 Pitching great Roger
25 Bandleader Herb ___
26 "Crud!"
27 Russian woman's name
28 Close, as a sleeping bag
29 Line on a weather map
30 Like people from Dublin
31 ___ a high note
35 ___ tape (band's submission)
37 Mini-scenes in a shoebox, e.g.
38 Cause abandoner
40 Make a mess of
41 Bordeaux boredom
43 Musician with a reed
44 Give more money than
47 Cherokee auto manufacturer
48 Norway's capital
49 Gets stuck, like a copier
50 E-mail command
51 Russian ruler: var.
52 Poet ___ Pound
53 Taps lightly
56 The Monkees' "___ Believer"
57 Kal ___ (pet food brand)

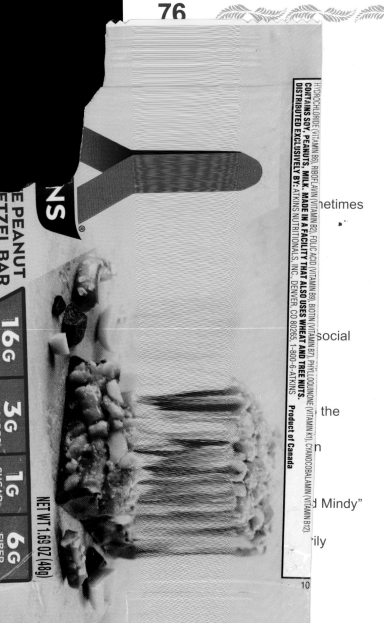

Soul Brothers

(Crossword grid)

Down

1. Octagonal sign
2. List type
3. Using as a perch
4. Ernie's pal
5. Black or Sherwood
6. Basra resident
7. Spaghetti sauce brand
8. Besides
9. James Cameron movie
10. Spice rack choice
11. Word in some law firm names
12. High schooler
13. Tee preceder
21. Lacks a choice
22. Take the helm
25. Sandal part
26. Pleasant inhalation
27. Broke down
28. Signs, as a contract
29. Singer Patsy
30. Railyard denizen
32. Simon medium
33. Female horses
35. Historical periods
36. Yale folk
38. "The Road Not Taken" poet
39. Dream stealer
44. Revolutionary groups
45. Dried fruits
47. Fencing ploy
48. Roger of movie reviews
49. Showed up
50. Indulge one's wanderlust
51. Village People hit
52. Baby carriage, in England
53. About 2.2 pounds
54. Thought
55. Barbershop call
56. Ad ___ committee

58. Astronaut Sally
59. Last in a series
60. Farm measurement
61. "Jeopardy!" name
62. Relinquishes
63. Gymnastics equipment
64. Medieval protection

Letter Drop

Across

1. Person in charge
5. Stomach muscles
8. Stuttgart-born philosopher
13. Cookie often twisted before eating
14. Prefix with political
15. "Slums of Beverly Hills" director Jenkins
16. Surfers wear them
18. Deodorant place
19. Orator's skills?
21. Chick's home
24. "We'll have a ___ old time"
25. Send out
26. Semiprecious gem used in sandpaper
28. Actor Rickman in "Harry Potter and the Sorcerer's Stone"
29. Computer company
32. Novels printed on the tops of buildings?
34. Campus women's org.
35. Israeli airline
36. "Man of a Thousand Faces" Chaney
37. Accompanying
38. X, in old Rome
39. Deserving of higher pay?
43. Grads-to-be, for short
44. Border
45. Wrote a song, perhaps
46. College head
47. Drink in the afternoon
48. Before, for Burns
49. Double-duty scissors for printers?
54. Stand for
55. Remove
59. Skips sounds, when speaking
60. Mao ___-tung
61. Grape's home
62. Redo a tuxedo
63. "___ XING" (street sign)
64. Finishes

Down

1. Let the audience applaud
2. Mine stuff
3. Prepared
4. Home run great Sammy
5. Shake up
6. Nickname for Elizabeth
7. Average
8. Dwelling monotonously (on)
9. Title otter in a 1977 Jim Henson TV special
10. Stare in amazement
11. Idle or Clapton
12. Thin wooden strip
15. Explorer for whom Australia's largest island is named
17. One who prods
20. Like lions and tigers, but not bears
21. Birds with beautiful plumes
22. Prison keeper, in Britain
23. Bad jokes elicit them
27. Jaguars' org.
28. Get ___ of one's own medicine
29. "This can't be my fault, right?"
30. Fuss
31. Dr. Jekyll's alter ego
33. Coordinates
37. Ironically funny
39. Get in with a stamped hand, maybe
40. Tried-and-true sayings
41. Brought on, like havoc
42. Chicago airport
46. Light on some calculators
47. Make fun of
49. Mental concoction
50. Carter of "Gimme a Break!"
51. Make leg warmers, e.g.
52. Letters before "://"
53. Rescue
56. Not a loss
57. Plus
58. "Uh-huh!"

None But the Brave

Across

1 Working away
5 Señor Arnaz
9 Explode
14 Doctors-in-training
16 Musical of "Tomorrow"
17 Getting ___ (aging)
18 Climber's respite
19 Bertolt Brecht title character
21 "Jewel Song," for one
22 Give ___ (sack)
23 Cutesy ending
26 File folder feature
29 Traffic cones
31 Rocket killer, briefly
34 Relaxes a bit
38 It has a Minor part
39 Al Capp detective
42 "Scarlett" setting
43 Comeback
44 1773 jetsam
45 Without obligation to buy
47 William Shatner title drug
49 Big Apple sch.
50 One of Chekhov's "Three Sisters"
54 "The Time Machine" race
58 Hal Foster's comics hero
62 Kind of balloon
64 Joseph of ___ (follower of Jesus)
65 "Me too!" relative
66 Potpourri piece, perhaps
67 Horse of the Year, 1960-64
68 Cain's nephew
69 Ernestine or Edith Ann

Down

1 Whiff
2 Barbershop quartet member
3 Last Supper question
4 GI's helmet
5 One or two bucks
6 Put on the books
7 Big name in brewing
8 Bone of contention
9 Brilliant assemblage
10 A thou
11 Banked
12 Cookie fruit
13 Doc's due
15 Turn red
20 Good terms
24 In reserve
25 "Venice of the Orient"
27 "Snafu" part
28 Bud holder?
30 Lassie's playmate
31 Gentle stream of song
32 Pal of Cecil the sea serpent
33 Bandicoot or wombat
35 Half a fly
36 Jet set jet
37 "The X-Files" whatsit
40 Knock on wood
41 Jeanne or Marie: abbr.
46 Estevez of "The Mighty Ducks"
48 "The Piano" costar Harvey
51 Alarm
52 Great blue wader
53 Dispatch boat
55 Christine of "Chicago Hope"
56 Shaq
57 Where to find Bologna
59 Hits head-on
60 "My Cup Runneth Over" singer
61 Drink from a dish
62 "Shame on you!"
63 Wade opponent

Child Stars

Across

1 Painter Chagall
5 Kofi Annan's country
10 ___ the crack of dawn
14 State where Orem and Moab are
15 Send to a specialist
16 "Finding ___"
17 Papa's mate
18 Mistake
19 Faucet trouble
20 Child star of "The Partridge Family"
23 Prof's helpers
24 One of the Ivy League colleges
25 Traffic light color
28 Frank Sinatra ex Gardner
31 Bird that mimics human speech
34 Child star of "Diff'rent Strokes"
37 Nashville sch.
38 The anti crowd
39 Peer pressure applier, perhaps
40 Sounds elicited by a masseuse
41 Historical period
42 Another child star of "Diff'rent Strokes"
44 Not length
46 Supporting vote
47 Barely visible to the naked eye
48 Italian goodbye
50 Male doll
51 Child star in "E.T."
57 "___ be a fool not to!"
58 Modern communication
59 Some particles
61 TV award
62 Mount for Moses
63 Fellow
64 Judicial garment
65 Bald bird
66 Pack carry-on luggage

Down

1 It's the word
2 Somewhat

3 Arthur C. Clarke's "Rendezvous with ___"
4 Sailors' songs
5 "___ Anatomy"
6 Sage or thyme
7 1970s hairstyle
8 Gas in glass
9 "Vast" group
10 In an excessive manner
11 Opinion poll stat
12 Pure Prairie League hit ballad
13 Outdo
21 Undercover cop
22 "___ Yankees"
25 Nixon veep who resigned
26 Native New Zealander
27 Part of a fairy tale trail
28 "She's ___" (Tom Jones song)
29 Cape ___ (country off the coast of Africa)

30 Microscopic critter: var.
32 Wan
33 Brazen woman
35 Prefix with meter
36 Abbr. on some sheet music
40 Throat glands
42 Winter-to-spring phenomenon
43 Twosome, tabloid-wise
45 Make clothes psychedelic
49 Overweight
50 "Can't Get You Out of My Head" singer Minogue
51 "___ arigato"
52 "What ___ mind reader?"
53 Phoned
54 Monetary unit of Iran
55 Disastrous defeat
56 Prefix meaning "within"
57 "___ So Bad" (Tom Petty tune)
60 Use a needle

Valentine's Nay

Across

1 Gorillalike
6 Former Big Apple ballpark
10 Grubby guy
14 The spirit of Russia?
15 Red-hunting org., ca. 1950
16 Emmett Kelly persona
17 K.T. of country
18 1984 Olympics boycotter
19 His career is in "Jeopardy!"
20 Response to "Will you be mine?"
23 Short snorts
24 Snockered
25 Comedienne Boosler
28 Long snort
30 An end to alcohol?
33 Placed, as wagers
34 Response to "Will you be mine?"
37 Casino maximum
39 Reason for an R rating
40 Prerecorded
41 Response to "Will you be mine?"
44 Ancient alphabetic symbol
45 Ready to go
46 Mortarboard sporter
47 Ray of "GoodFellas"
49 Bagged beverage
50 Huckleberry or Mickey
51 Response to "Will you be mine?"
58 Bad to the bone
59 1969 landing site
60 Jazz pianist Blake
61 Bucolic byway
62 Lindros of hockey
63 Skater Boitano
64 Make like a muscleman
65 Russo of "Tin Cup"
66 Long lock

Down

1 Say it's so
2 Ritzy
3 Thumb-twiddling
4 Swim sans suit
5 Submit to the teacher
6 Eschews
7 Corn holder
8 Leisure
9 Kind of paint
10 Treat unfairly, in slang
11 Act the couch potato
12 Act the robot
13 Kind of camera or canyon
21 Candid
22 The eyes have it
25 New York Harbor island
26 "Mule Train" singer Frankie
27 Shoot for
28 Trusty mount
29 Like candles
30 Database fodder
31 "___ of a Woman" (Pacino film)
32 Whom Jason jilted
35 Greek peak
36 First Vice President never to be President
38 Princeton mascot
42 Kelsey of "Frasier"
43 Literary Lamb
48 Hooked by a shark?
49 E-mail predecessor
50 Where to find pickets
51 Face shape
52 It's creepy
53 Days of knights?
54 Bump off
55 Award bestowed by "The Village Voice"
56 "Buenos ___"
57 Hankerings
58 Little rascal

Double Your Fun

Across

1 Photographer Adams
6 Knocks on the head
10 Pool or pit start
14 Chocolate bean
15 Ominous phrase
16 It's taken with a hand in the air
17 Ex-bandmate of Lennon and McCartney
18 Long division word
19 On a cruise ship
20 Play where Desdemona gets sucked into a tornado?
23 Tons
24 Rhythmic contraction of the heart
25 Earth tones
28 5, for some golf holes
29 Place to find infested confections?
36 Fail to know the words, maybe
37 Deserves it
38 Vote on C-SPAN
39 Military tactic designed to confuse?
44 One of 100 in D.C.
45 "In ___ and out the other"
46 1980s mall hangouts
50 "You're ___ much trouble!"
51 Item that'll rarely catch a rodent?
55 ___ fixe
56 Hair feature
57 Radiant
59 Hunted animal
60 "What ___ can I say?"
61 "___ a break!"
62 Long stretch
63 Those things in Tijuana
64 Slackens

Down

1 Summer coolers, for short
2 Org. the USA is part of
3 "Beat it!"
4 Aviation's Amelia
5 Lurer on the Rhine
6 Put up, as a house
7 Mr. Bill's exclamation
8 Annie of "Ghostbusters"
9 Ostentatious
10 Like stretches of highway on the water
11 New Jersey city next to Newark
12 Bridge material
13 Play nice, maybe
21 Go completely nuts
22 2002 Eddie Murphy/ Owen Wilson movie
25 Eight, in Havana
26 Overthrow
27 Television set, back in the day
30 Show starring William L. Petersen
31 Excitement
32 "The Sound of Music" extra
33 Prepare filets
34 "The Lion King" character
35 Garment worker
40 They bring up baby
41 Garcia or Griffith
42 Acting, in a way
43 Savannah's state
46 To the left or the right
47 Cowboy's event
48 Pageant host
49 Grim Reaper's collection
50 Spots in the sea
52 ___ Minor (constellation)
53 Handouts for the poor
54 Fleshy fruit
58 "Rushmore" director Anderson

O, K!

Across

1 Type measurements
6 Asian sea
10 Czech or Pole
14 Igloo dweller
15 Poet Teasdale
16 Two less than octa-
17 13th-century tough guy
19 Woodsman's stock
20 Stat for Greg Maddux
21 M.D. colleagues
22 Easily
24 Had a feeling
26 Jackson of country
27 Santa alias
33 Flower
36 Buzzing insect
37 Bill addition
38 Pays to play
40 Top, say
41 Said "!@#$%&!"
43 Presley's label
44 Hooded pullover
47 Signs the contract
48 Cartoon police
51 Susan's "Dead Man Walking" costar
52 Scam
56 Full-price payer
59 London wear
60 Misrepresentation
61 Court zero
62 "A Fish Called Wanda" Oscar-winner
65 Employer
66 Verve
67 Smooth
68 Listening devices
69 E-mail word
70 Pitchers

Down

1 ___ Peak
2 Accustom (to)
3 Cigar type
4 Be abed
5 Gawking sort
6 Sets a price
7 Stands cheer
8 Swift horse
9 Ship's rope
10 High priest
11 City of Massachusetts or Virginia
12 Figure skating maneuver
13 Flower home
18 Pertaining to the Subcontinent
23 Another name for a crook
25 Ione of "Say Anything"
28 Squash, perhaps
29 XX
30 Palindromic vessel
31 Whimsical mission
32 Alimony receivers
33 Place in Monopoly
34 Fairy tale starter
35 Spends the night
39 Bad guy
42 Will-o'-the-___
45 Peacenik's slogan
46 Sunnis hold it sacred
49 They're under cities
50 Picnic side
53 Drab shade of green
54 Of a higher class
55 Gets hands-on experience
56 Elmer's product
57 Civil rights figure Parks
58 Soccer legend
59 Matter topper
63 Moving need
64 Kareem, once

Home Plate

Across

1 Non-union worker
5 Chicken
9 "In-A-___-Da-Vida"
14 Zeus's wife and sister
15 Cincinnati's state
16 Mixtures
17 Fancy lad's interjection
18 Howard and Paul
19 Easy jigsaw pieces to start with
20 Phrase on Idaho license plates
23 Three-in-one
24 "Oh, well" response
25 Hwy.
27 Response to a knock at the door
28 How-___ (guides)
30 One of five on a foot
32 Does a baking task
34 They may require a fee
35 Phrase on New Hampshire license plates
40 "What ___ you thinking?!"
41 "The Taming of the Shrew" city
42 Clearly shows
46 2,000 pounds
47 "As I see it," in chat rooms
50 Put down
51 Skin lotion stuff
53 Like Russian matryoshka dolls
55 Phrase on California license plates
58 Farr or Kennedy
59 Wood shop gripper
60 Tatiana and Laila
61 Fab Ringo
62 List-ending abbr.
63 Speakeasy drinks
64 Elaine's last name, on "Seinfeld"
65 Jewish place of worship
66 Lady ___ (pop star)

Down

1 Tough to trust
2 Lucrezia Borgia's brother
3 Estee Lauder fragrance line
4 Louisiana feature
5 In an inferior situation
6 "Rooty Tooty Fresh and Fruity" restaurant, for short
7 King who had the Labyrinth built
8 Sticky note brand
9 "Faust" writer
10 Former Italian PM and kidnapping victim ___ Moro
11 The technically savvy
12 Sits in prison
13 Silly animal
21 Loosen a shoelace
22 A long time ___
26 Ernie of golf
29 Narrow waterway: abbr.
31 Nothing, in Nicaragua
32 Cinematographer Nykvist
33 Back-to-school mo.
35 Float in the air
36 Dubliner, e.g.
37 Devour
38 Chris in the "Batman" sequels
39 Norse letters
40 Got hitched
43 NBA players, in slang
44 "Strange Magic" band
45 Finishes the puzzle
47 Florence's country, to natives
48 Portioning (out)
49 City of Ukraine or Texas
52 Archie Bunker's wife
54 Legendary football coach Amos Alonzo ___
56 36-down's country, to poets
57 Jacob's twin, in the Bible
58 Major Baroque composer's monogram

The Bugs Stopped Here

Across

1. Mutt's mate
5. Palindromic pop quartet
9. Aboveboard
14. Jai tail?
15. Montgomery and Rommel
16. Jordan's only seaport
17. Teri of "After Hours"
18. Hooters
19. Mint ___
20. Region of Nicaragua
23. Phone beginner
24. Phone
25. "Viva Zapata!" star
28. It may be hard to swallow
29. Yahoo
32. Julie in "Dr. Zhivago"
33. Where to find secondhand rows
36. West of Gotham City?
37. Real Quiet bit
38. Slave of opera
39. "Romper Room" urging
43. Grable or Gable
44. "The Nanny" has three of them
45. Deadly shark
46. Like certain teenage turtles
48. "The Music Man" setting
49. Greek salad chunks
50. Groucho in "Duck Soup"
55. Priestley of "Love and Death on Long Island"
56. Half a Chinese circle
57. Levels a Luger
59. Inclined
60. Grimm beginning
61. "Chariots of Fire" finale
62. Droplets
63. Sounds of disgust
64. Film format for tall tales?

Down

1. Bender
2. Jack who played Jake in "Big Bad John"
3. Casino game
4. Bob, Ted, Carol, or Alice
5. In conflict with
6. He was a knife guy
7. Big swig
8. Marx, to Engels
9. UC-San Diego site
10. One, to one
11. Hoedown honeys
12. "A likely story!"
13. Beer barrel poker
21. Proof letters
22. Unflappable
25. Cutting edge
26. Unwelcome house gas
27. Gaza Strippers
28. He sang "Beauty And The Beast" with Celine
29. Wakayama woofer
30. Chair on poles
31. Genesis
34. Words of admiration
35. Haile Selassie, to some
40. Adds up
41. ___ Butler (voice of Huckleberry Hound, Chilly Willy, et al.)
42. Comes out of hiding
47. All-purpose truck, for short
48. Poker concession
49. "To Kill a Mockingbird" lawyer Atticus
50. Number of prime interest
51. Voice of America org.
52. Phyllis Diller's "husband"
53. Neeson of "Nell"
54. 1978 Village People hit
55. Bowe blow
58. Safe or fair follower

Letters From Abroad

Across

1 Jeans maker Strauss
5 Kid's play brick
9 Olivia of "The Wonder Years"
13 Somewhat
14 Got wind of
15 Yours and mine
16 One of the Three Bears
17 See things the same
18 Not very funny
19 They need to dominate
21 Visit
22 Particle that's emitted
23 Site: abbr.
24 Lord ___ of poetry
25 Road gunk
27 Indie/electronica group formed in Edinburgh
30 "Yeah, right!"
32 Enzyme suffix
33 "High Sierra" actress Lupino
34 Rising trend, on a graph
36 Little Leaguer, to his parents
40 Bathroom, in London
41 That cruise ship
42 Round building for grain storage
43 Medical picture-taker
48 Drift into dreamland
49 Sign outside a studio door
50 ___ de mer (seasickness)
51 "Who'll Stop the Rain" band
53 Plant with fronds
54 Bluto's place on campus, in a movie
58 Jane Austen character
59 Comic DeGeneres
60 Roadie's equipment
61 Civil disturbance
62 Docks
63 Dirty material
64 Fill to the top
65 Takes the tab
66 Daly of "Gypsy"

Down

1 The Dalai ___
2 List-ending abbr.
3 Like a lot of Anne Rice subjects
4 Neighbor of Montana
5 Courtroom jargon
6 Site for piercings
7 Country common to the theme answers
8 Pindar poems
9 Waiters pack them
10 Illinois or Colorado city
11 Englishman
12 Donny & Marie's surname
14 Parma or Black Forest
20 "Them!" creature
24 "Mama's Gun" singer Erykah
25 Nineteenth of a relevant alphabet
26 Snake on the Nile
28 Chaos
29 Floor worker
31 Explode with violence
35 Tiger's sound
36 Trail stops
37 Trick-taking game
38 Prog-rock legends
39 Fisherman's pole
41 "Daily Affirmations" host Stuart
43 Personal assistants, often
44 Sickle-cell ___
45 Animal whose name means "mountain mouse"
46 First name in flying
47 German's outburst
52 Shoreline
54 Actor Johnny
55 Ques. response
56 Twirled (around)
57 90 degrees from norte

I'm Awfully Font Of You

Across

1 Rapper ___ Shakur
6 Haberdashery items
10 Secretive govt. branch
13 Clean pots
14 "Yeah, tell me another one!"
15 Burden
17 Give the slip
18 Equipment
19 When tripled, a 1970 war film
20 Font-based actress?
23 JFK stats
24 Work function invitees
25 Where mil. planes land
28 Env. attachment
30 "Star Wars" project of the 1980s
31 Unlike a coward
33 Penny or quarter
35 Santa's little helpers
39 Teddy Roosevelt's advice to a printer?
42 Play the mandolin
43 One who gives the once-over
44 Himalayan creature
45 Take blades to the blades
47 Tiny particle
49 Got the biggest trophy
50 Plaintiff's filing
54 Two, in Germany
56 Bob Marley's typographical declaration?
60 "And a lot of others besides that," in four letters
61 With a cast of thousands
62 Office powder
64 Farm structure
65 Actor Green of the "Austin Powers" series
66 Mom's brother
67 Console to play Super Mario Bros. on
68 Elm or oak
69 One of 150 in the Bible

Down

1 Mao ___-tung
2 Home of the Bruins
3 Do some bartending
4 Actor/soldier Murphy
5 Come up with
6 Video game achievement
7 Busy as ___
8 The Dallas Cowboys and the Washington Redskins
9 Pieces of bacon
10 Phrase in many "Law & Order" scripts
11 Makes flakes
12 Radiations of light
16 Puts into words
21 Jousting weapon
22 Lymph ___
25 Fundamentals
26 30.48 centimeters
27 Hazy image
29 North African nation whose capital is Tripoli
32 Certain musical interludes
34 Philosopher Friedrich
36 Opinion
37 Prefix with plasm
38 Body covering
40 "Don't include me"
41 Escalates
46 Most sagacious
48 Get together
50 False statements
51 "Lord of the Rings" actor Sean
52 Huge mammal of the sea
53 Get to the point?
55 Some golf clubs
57 Evening, on a marquee
58 Ancient Peruvian
59 Took a header
63 "Everybody Hurts" band

Middle Names

Across

1 Mooches
5 "Oh, Heavenly Dog" dog
10 Wisecrack
14 Element element
15 City SSE of Buffalo
16 Part of Caesar's reproach
17 Trumpet accessory
18 "Sing Along With ___"
19 Impulse
20 Baker's middle name?
23 "Nightmare" street
24 Beginning bits
25 "No doubt about it!"
27 Bone-connecting tissue
31 Auto mechanic's middle name?
35 ___ decimal system
39 Response to the Little Red Hen
40 "The balcony is closed" critic
42 Othello's nemesis
43 "How Do I Live" singer Rimes
45 Homebuilder's middle name?
47 Takes one's time
49 Mr. Magoo's dog
52 Nigerian civil war site, 1967-70
57 "The Loco-Motion" singer Little ___
58 Cupid's middle name?
62 Turner of Tinseltown
64 "The Last Picture Show" locale
65 Corporate image
66 Old Fords
67 "Enough!"
68 Persia, today
69 "___, right"
70 "Drop Dead Fred" actress Phoebe
71 Bound bundle

Down

1 Stag film?
2 Complete reversal
3 Choral composition
4 Sling mud
5 Bikini or Alamogordo, for example
6 Director/producer Kazan
7 Jersey five
8 DJ Wolfman
9 "Psst!" follower
10 Torah studier
11 Merman or Mertz
12 Flick pic
13 Toddler's middle name?
21 '96 Senate resignee
22 Work the bar
26 Cooked one's own goose?
28 The Bee Gees brothers
29 Bailiwicks
30 Streep of "The River Wild"
31 "Not Ready for Prime Time Players" pgm.
32 "The Purloined Letter" writer
33 One-time link
34 Olympic symbol
36 Bunch of bills
37 Big item in Hollywood?
38 "That hurts!"
41 Ground-rule double award
44 Christmas carol
46 Cry of triumph
48 Titillating
49 Santa's middle name?
50 Shaped like Humpty Dumpty
51 Jamie Lee Curtis's 1988 fish
53 Extemporize
54 Plants
55 Princely
56 Unanimously
59 Former Chevy
60 Way out
61 Order for dinner
63 Grate stuff

TV Personalities

Across

1 Boom or gaff
5 Sips the chowder, clamorously
11 Squeeze
14 Kind of duck
15 Liquid high in monounsaturated fatty acids
16 "Gotcha!"
17 Cinches or clinches
18 "The Wizard of Oz" prop
19 Holiday quaff
20 "Bedroom at Arles" painter
23 Ultimate purpose
24 Pitt of "Kalifornia"
25 Table wines
26 Wharton grad
29 Wishful words
32 Solo player of '60s TV
35 Mayberry letters
38 Scrape together
39 Word usually put in brackets
40 "Deadeye Dick" author
45 6/6/44 beachhead
46 Reggae's precursor
47 Hooded windbreaker
51 Art Spiegelman's comic rodent
53 Prevailed
54 Third-century Christian martyr
58 Sense of humor
59 Car bar
60 Lichen component
61 "Arabian Nights" name
62 Novel ending
63 Striped pros
64 "The Mayor of Simpleton" art-rockers
65 Stand for
66 Together, musically

Down

1 Chip off the old block
2 "Glengarry Glen Ross" star
3 Changes for the better
4 Knight in shining armor
5 Teacake
6 Brest milk
7 "The Runnin' Rebels" of the Big West
8 Cape ___ (westernmost point of continental Europe)
9 Backup procedure
10 Red wine + fruit juice + soda water
11 Despicable individuals
12 "I'm in trouble now!"
13 Practical joke
21 Tiger-in-your-tank brand
22 It's northwest of Molokai
26 Stands for
27 Precipice
28 Discombobulated
30 Frat letter
31 Ltr. extra
33 Bart, to Maggie
34 Act the couch potato
35 "Citizen Kane" studio
36 Giant syllable
37 Theatrical
41 Eastern cuisine
42 Widely praised
43 Conversant with
44 Clarion blast
48 Muddied the water
49 David Carradine series of the '70s
50 Hanging loose
52 R.E.M. vocalist Michael
53 Piece of cake
54 Channel choker
55 Marble streak
56 Alice's Thanksgiving Day guest
57 Pirates' pelf
58 Ear-y stuff

Scenes From a Mall

Across

1 Largest continent
5 "Cagney & Lacey" actress ___ Daly
9 Swiss ___ (vegetable)
14 Drive-___ (fast food restaurant feature)
15 Sheep's coat
16 Button ___ (sewing machine fixture)
17 Where free samples are dispensed at a mall
19 Take down a notch
20 Guitarist Lofgren
21 Standing against
23 Prickly plants
25 See it the same way
27 Big beer holder
28 Suffix meaning "sort of"
29 Mall business that believes change is a good thing
32 With an even score
34 Not max.
35 Delighted sound
36 Mall fixture where you can ask questions
42 ___ Guevara
43 "This ___ joke, right?"
44 Latin words to a traitor
45 They surround shopping malls
50 "Ben-___"
51 Devoured dinner
52 White from fright
53 Fail to be
55 Tecumseh's tribe
57 Seaweed extract
58 Lucky number
59 Mall occupants, often
64 January, to Mexicans
65 Furniture wood
66 Responses to fireworks
67 Burdened (with)
68 Vegetable often served fried
69 Not speedy

Down

1 Treasury Dept. branch
2 Cable TV abbr.
3 TV cooking show
4 IRS probe
5 Yahtzee category
6 Not me
7 Neither here ___ there
8 Matador's opponent
9 Adult supervisor
10 Train stowaway
11 Largest U.S. state
12 Do more planting
13 River bottom dragger
18 154, in Ancient Rome
22 Heavy jacket worn by sailors
23 ___ Field (Mets' ballpark)
24 X ___ "x-ray"
25 Hit song from Sarah McLachlan
26 Non-Jew
30 Huge
31 Secret language
33 Pier
37 Fleetwood Mac hit of 1976
38 "The Heat ___"
39 Otherworldly
40 Shock momentarily, as with news
41 Author Vonnegut
45 Big group of something
46 Wise Greek goddess
47 Plundered
48 Elvis Presley's "In the ___"
49 Epic tale
54 Ravi Shankar songs
56 "Where ___ you?"
57 "Put Your Head on My Shoulder" singer Paul
60 "A mouse!!!"
61 Listening device?
62 Greek letter
63 Direction away from NNE

You Already Said That

Across

1 Casual language
6 City where the Taj Mahal is
10 Self-satisfied
14 HR worker, often
15 Study at the last second
16 Short and to the point
17 Redundant cash dispenser
19 Scandinavian city
20 Rushing noises
21 "Shall we?" response
23 "That's neither here ___ there"
24 Redundant records
28 Key near F1
29 Feedbag bit
30 Jeans with a mascot named Buddy
31 Mr. Arnaz
34 "Stop!"
37 Feminine component, in Jungian psychology
39 Doubly-redundant incentive
42 Fixes, as for illnesses
43 It may be uncharted
44 Crux
45 Palindromic city about 60 miles from Oklahoma City
46 Wind dir.
48 DJ's plays, once
50 Redundant amount
54 How old you are
57 Two gelcaps, maybe
58 On empty, for real
60 Contraction before "It'll be fun!"
62 Redundant outcomes
64 Nativity figures
65 Fiery interest
66 Ham it up
67 Part of CD
68 Like some sushi bar food
69 Affix, as a button

Down

1 Basketball's Kemp
2 Printed piece of art, for short
3 Knight's protection
4 "Finding ___" (2003 film)
5 Understands fully
6 Muscle pains
7 Miller's stuff
8 Didn't walk
9 Pilot Earhart
10 Actor Baio
11 Italian dictator
12 Web address, for short
13 Ronny & the Daytonas hit
18 Latin dance
22 Abbr. on a cornerstone
25 Good thing to buy in Monopoly
26 "Song of the South" Uncle
27 It makes bread rise
28 Dublin's land
31 Coffee in an orange-handled pot
32 Give off, as charm
33 1971 Peckinpah film with Dustin Hoffman
35 French send-off
36 The Mormons: abbr.
38 December drinks
40 Orgs.
41 Erase data
47 Need a tissue
49 Non-poetic writing forms
51 Column style
52 Like some jazz or folk songs
53 Big, like a lumberjack
54 Radiant
55 Cat, in Cagliari
56 City on the Ruhr River (hidden in DELICATESSENS)
59 Show you're mad
60 Mil. officer's charge
61 ___ tai (fun drink)
63 French word for "born," seen before a maiden name

The Emperor's New Clothes

Across

1 Neckerchief
6 Exploding star
10 Reassuring words
14 Toward Marie Byrd Land
15 "The Emperor's New Clothes," for example
17 Like the Emperor
19 Like films before "The Jazz Singer"
20 Meadow murmur
21 Ofc. computer link
22 "Can I take that as ___?"
23 Cardigan canine
26 Gala get-together
27 Words of resignation
29 Like the Emperor
32 Morse morsel
33 Area of a circle = ___-squared
34 Kitty
35 Like the Emperor
40 Potential perch or pike
41 Fish story
42 Jenny "The Swedish Nightingale"
44 Like the Emperor
48 Burton of the new "Star Trek"
49 "Stalag 17" denizens
50 Car bomb?
52 Pet Shop Boys record label
53 H, to Homer
54 Monkey's uncle, maybe
56 "Duke of Earl" or "Get a Job," stylistically
58 Like the Emperor
62 Tailor-made guidelines for the Royal Put-On?
63 More dreadful
64 Lip-___
65 Group of toads
66 Run-down

Down

1 "To repeat..."
2 Meathead, to Archie
3 Run wild
4 "Top ___ mornin' to you"
5 From that point on
6 Eagles' org.
7 Meal opener
8 Stern strings
9 Thessaly-to-Colchis craft
10 One of the Addams family
11 "The Song of the Earth" composer Gustav
12 Fatty acid salt
13 Corny bit
16 Longbow wood
18 Z preceder?
24 Word with dance or date
25 Babbled, as a brook
26 Vain
28 Brittle bits
30 Semicircular recess
31 Male mouser
33 Berth place
36 Brisbane bounder
37 Benefits
38 Ball of fire
39 Bewitched
43 Wash-and-wear
44 Topples
45 ___ public
46 Stir
47 "Ethan Frome" star
48 Lime Street insurance giant
51 Writer LeShan
54 Pitches
55 Rat or brat follower
57 Tony's cousin
59 PC tilde topper
60 Bother or pother
61 F-15, for one

Witch Hunt

Across

1 Top site for junk?
6 Worldwide: abbr.
10 Mischievous moppets
14 Egypt's capital
15 "Quite contrary" lass
16 Ram, for one
17 "Wonderful, wonderful" city of song
19 Frigate's front
20 Urban haze
21 Awaits a birth
23 Military training acad.
26 Before, to Blake
27 Piece from the past
28 Eggheads
30 Señor's emphatic yes
31 Popular, and then some
34 Paves the way?
35 Harrow's rival
37 Make blank
39 Quitter's cry
41 Witch hidden in this puzzle's theme entries
42 "Eat hearty!"
43 Scandinavian toast
44 Lhasa ___ (Tibetan dog)
46 Julie in "Dr. Zhivago"
47 Psychic's sight
48 Vintners' vessels
50 Earn
52 No-goodniks
54 Oil additive letters
55 D-day troop carrier
56 Makes tracks
58 Verdi opera
60 Gymnast Korbut
61 Thick floor covering
66 Oversupply
67 Triumphant cry
68 Take a nibble
69 Get smart?
70 Comedian Laurel
71 Say "y'all," say

Down

1 Duke's conf.
2 Chinese "way"
3 Stockbroker's steer
4 Ticks off
5 Dupe dupers
6 Publicist's concern
7 Backseat driver, e.g.
8 Elder age indicators?
9 Canadian wildcats
10 John Hancock Tower designer
11 Met mural painter
12 Story line
13 Hems, say
18 Kentucky Derby contender
22 Practiced, as a trade
23 Thickheaded
24 Grouches
25 Sculpted coffin
29 Madonna's "La ___ Bonita"
30 Afternoon TV fare
32 Egyptian underworld god
33 Rent payer
36 "We're all done here"
38 Small stream
40 Santa's little helpers
45 Eye-related
49 Slates of elite invitees
51 News bulletin
53 Les ___-Unis
54 "Cosmos" creator Carl
56 Cranberry sites
57 Jazzy Fitzgerald
59 Asia's ___ Sea
62 Toothpaste tube letters
63 Trident-shaped letter
64 J.F.K. advisory
65 Casual top

Reel Fruit Flavor

Across

1 Japanese seaport or dog
6 Invigorate
11 Watering hole
14 "Lady Love" singer Lou
15 Sun screen?
16 Receiver abbr.
17 Malcolm McDowell satire of '71, with "A"
20 Party animal?
21 Sudden invasion
22 Their man in Havana
23 Here-there connector
24 Open-books exams
25 Godfrey Cambridge serio-comedy of '71
31 Short art course?
32 Send through channels
33 Steely, as nerves
36 Meet moguls
37 Piece of history
39 Discern
40 Crony
41 Cheated, so to speak
42 Europe's largest volcano
43 Henry Fonda film of '40, with "The"
47 Jerry's ex, on "Seinfeld"
49 Cry of discovery
50 Attack
51 Largest city in Africa
54 Dazzle
57 Bob Hope film of '51
60 Audio receiver
61 Cox of "Beverly Hills Cop"
62 Like a new penny
63 Fourth-yr. folks
64 Rip off
65 "Fatha" of jazz

Down

1 Keystone structure
2 Headless cabbage
3 Triumphant taunt
4 Mom's forte, for short
5 Solicit
6 Shoddy
7 II Chronicles follower
8 Dawdling
9 Crazy Eights cousin
10 It makes scents
11 Revolutionary of '79
12 Sound of Seattle
13 Skaters' 540s
18 Spineless one
19 Ethiopian of opera
23 Basketball trophy of sorts
24 Chip in chips
25 Waist variety
26 "My Way" lyricist
27 Aggressive drivers, often
28 Get the lead out
29 Takes long strides
30 Show up
34 Copper
35 One third of a Fab Four refrain
37 Sports fans, often
38 Optimist's asset
42 Gay Nineties, e.g.
44 Omani money
45 Klinger player
46 Rushing sound
47 Rob of "Melrose Place"
48 "The Merry Widow" composer Franz
51 Heavenly Hash holder
52 "I" of "The King and I"
53 Romantic interlude
54 Cut from the same cloth
55 Khayyám quaff
56 Ben & Jerry's alternative
58 Bon ___
59 Fraternity letter

Pear Bonding

Across

1 Campers
4 Bait and switch, for one
8 "Forget it!"
14 "ER" setting
15 "Is this a dagger which ___..." (Macbeth)
16 Father of geometry
17 Opera by Bizet
20 It could get you down
21 Swahili or Zulu
22 Lead
25 Noodle
29 King David's predecessor
30 Sailors' safekeeper
32 IBM bailout option
35 They're fired as soon as they're employed
37 Outpouring of gossip
38 "The Hay Wain" painter, for one
42 Beethoven's Third Symphony
43 Rameses, in "The Ten Commandments"
44 Harriet Stowe, ___ Beecher
45 Persian pleasure
46 Thrill
49 Lt. Kojak
50 Like rabbits and hounds
55 "Calvin and Hobbes" girl
58 Garlic mayonnaise
59 It's the ultimate "Poof!"
64 Savvy
65 Armed Forces VIP
66 Warmed the bench
67 Something to spare?
68 He drove Miss Daisy
69 Give it a whirl

Down

1 ___ of passage
2 TV monitor of sorts
3 Napped kid
4 "High ___" (Bogart film)
5 1860s insignia
6 Ireland's ___ Lingus
7 "Purlie" star Moore
8 "Schindler's List" turndown
9 Give the boot
10 "The Unfinished Symphony" composer
11 Word a toreador adores
12 Football center?
13 Peace-keeping bodies: abbr.
18 Some have black eyes
19 It's in one year and out the other
23 Roadside auto part?
24 It's off Corsica
26 Impish
27 Beguile
28 "Lorenzo's Oil" star
30 Shrink-wrap, e.g.
31 Patch pitch
32 Chosen but not yet installed
33 Jazz vocalist Vaughan
34 Five double-sawbucks
36 Follett ferret
39 Crichton critter
40 "Nova" subj.
41 Dollar rival
47 Spirit raiser?
48 Nixon chief of staff
50 "A pox upon thee!"
51 "...Rich and Famous" emcee
52 Affront-filled fete
53 Dana of "The Sting"
54 Simple song
56 Plotting
57 Made tracks
59 High-tech recording medium
60 Bull or fool follower
61 Jeanne d'Arc, for one: abbr.
62 City "by the sea, oh"
63 Publicity, so to speak

Flight Information

Across

1 Lovers' quarrels
6 Drainage spot
11 That guy
14 Use
15 Author Norman Vincent ___
16 "Pulp Fiction" actress Thurman
17 Church no-no
19 Calendar abbr.
20 Volleyball player's equipment
21 Emerson's "Circles," for instance
23 Winter Olympics event
24 Swarms
26 Bacon units
29 Public house
30 Engages in pillaging
31 Stood toe-to-toe with
32 Reporter's query
35 "Dear" woman?
36 Fraternity/sorority gathering
37 Hoax
38 Designer of the Rock and Roll Hall of Fame
39 Michelangelo masterpiece
40 Comic Mandel
41 Family tree members
43 Reserved in advance
44 Majestic homes
46 Punching hand
47 Scene of conflict
48 Acorns, someday
52 Bering or Barents
53 Two on a par five
56 The middle X of XXX
57 Stand for Picasso
58 Climb
59 Baseball bat wood
60 Doesn't say "hit me"
61 Family car

Down

1 What a prankster puts on a chair
2 Lendl of the court
3 Token payment?
4 Faithfulness
5 Goofs
6 Heart companion
7 Slippery swimmers
8 Isn't any more
9 QB Manning
10 Didn't pay up
11 Bruce Willis film
12 Clarifying words
13 New York landmark
18 Henpecks
22 Paul McCartney's title
24 Did up one's shoes
25 Anytime
26 Give a hand?
27 One option for Hamlet
28 He hosted "Lifestyles of the Rich and Famous"
29 Bus alternatives
31 Abraham Lincoln's money
33 Dust Bowl denizen
34 Garden worry
36 Medieval weapon
37 Steeplechase, for one
39 Millennium hundredths
40 Restaurant seater
42 James Bond creator Fleming
43 Kid transport
44 Ziti, e.g.
45 Spheres
46 Idaho ___, Idaho
48 Do as told
49 Posh exclamation
50 Singer Fitzgerald
51 Spotted
54 Bit of food for Seattle Slew
55 Springsteen's "Born in the ___"

96

However Often

Across

1. Crook's other name
6. Therefore
10. Half a dance
13. Oblong fruit
14. Keaton of "Annie Hall"
15. Ticket information
16. Type of opportunity
19. These may be inflated
20. Last Greek letter
21. Iowa State University's town
22. Rose's home, maybe
23. 24-hour current events channel
24. Blue shade
26. Franklin of R&B
28. Skin feature
30. War locale, for short
31. They clear the bases
33. Public humiliation
35. Old yarn
38. Belgian treaty city
39. Loves to death
40. ___ Palmas, Spain
41. Start of a Shakespeare title
43. Horrified
47. Canada's capital
49. Wilbur, in "Charlotte's Web"
50. Doubting Thomas's comment
51. Served perfectly
52. Yogurt variety
55. Ice cream parlor sight
56. Commodores hit
59. Sushi ingredient, often
60. Word on a doghouse
61. Less covered
62. Like some martinis
63. Summit
64. Tennis star Agassi

Down

1. One-celled organism
2. German golfer Bernhard
3. Secretly sent, sometimes
4. Gets on in years
5. "___ Married an Axe Murderer" (Mike Myers film)
6. Kitchen floor piece, perhaps
7. Former Defense Secretary Alexander
8. Lopsided, as an advantage
9. Spot
10. Pen person
11. Fan's favorite event
12. "Cool!"
14. "___ Yankees"
17. Lacking fame
18. Small dollop
23. Southern tribe
25. Golden years fund
27. Slender
28. Spurs to action
29. Scandinavian capital
32. End-of-list abbr.
34. Chopped meal
35. Prime minister before Major
36. Like some winds
37. Empties the tub
38. Was a bad winner
42. Mobile computer
44. On the train
45. Workshop tool
46. "___ here!" ("Poltergeist" catchphrase)
48. Ending for lemon or lime
49. Dock
53. Not taped
54. Visa rival, for short
55. Family
57. Historian's time
58. Lawyer's gp.

Spaghetti Western

Across

1 Lampooned
7 Ship partition
15 Comfortable
16 "Betsy's Wedding" actor
17 Banana Bananza! Bar purveyor
19 Get "altared"
20 Cone head?
21 Tannery tool
22 Society's woes
24 Three-seater
27 Words of woe
31 Twist and pinch
33 "The Innocents Abroad" author
36 Make tracks
38 In ___ of (for)
39 Half a Merrick musical
40 1958 remake of "The Asphalt Jungle"
43 "Cry ___ River"
44 Cookie king Wally
45 B'Elanna ___, Chief Engineer of "Star Trek: Voyager"
47 Henry Fonda's WWII Lieut. jg
50 Laughing
51 "College GameDay" home
52 Thick fog
54 Naldi of the Ziegfeld Follies
55 Tail tirelessly
58 "7 Faces of Dr. ___"
60 Pc. of the whole
61 Hans Christian Andersen tale
67 Prerequisite perusal
68 Stupefied state
69 Capital of the Cowboy State
70 Planned Parenthood founder Margaret

Down

1 Joined at the table
2 "Pinky" Oscar nominee
3 Incisive
4 It's game
5 GI hangouts
6 Drudges
7 "Foiled again!"
8 "The Subject Was Roses" director Grosbard
9 Mongolian monk
10 Have no doubts
11 Jean of the screen
12 Stately shader
13 Critic ___ Louise Huxtable
14 "Hey Nineteen" rockers Steely ___
18 Apocalypse
23 Stuff to the gills
25 Vigorously begins
26 "Summertime," for one
28 Scary
29 Conversational cutoff point, often
30 Rock producer Brian
32 Steak on a stick
34 Lane partner
35 Henry VIII's house
37 Mia, Nia, or Pia
41 "Hannie Caulder" actress Diana
42 Emerald Isle
43 Marseilles Mrs.
46 Reel
48 Working
49 "Star Trek" helmsman
53 NATO and SEATO
56 Bogeyman
57 "Glengarry ___ Ross"
59 Creole veggie
61 HBO alternative
62 "Whazzat?"
63 -speak
64 TV chef Martin
65 Five-star '50s monogram
66 Linked-computers acronym

Lose It …

Across

1. "Right on the nose!"
6. Leave in the lurch
10. Stowe tow
14. Festoon
15. Two-tone treat
16. Surfing mecca
17. You can take his word for it
18. "___ of the Spider Woman"
19. Sucker play
20. ...like a pancake server?
23. A shot
24. Proverbs
27. White key key
31. Govt. health watchdog
32. One of "Them!"
33. ...like a sauna operator?
36. Former long-distance letters
37. Oscar's cousin
38. Kernel's quarters
39. "Let's go!"
40. Pooh pal
41. ...like a bartender?
45. Collection agcy.
46. Means of escape
47. Goofy creator
48. Mount Olympus is its highest peak
50. 1951 Scrooge player Alastair
51. ...like Michelangelo?
58. Novelist Waugh
60. "Field of Dreams" setting
61. Schlemiel
62. Fir coat?
63. Red or Card, for short
64. "The Zoo Story" playwright
65. Former loves
66. "Looking for Mr. Goodbar" actor Richard
67. Lecherous

Down

1. Pointed remark
2. Sacred cow
3. Canceled, to NASA
4. Got bigger
5. "___ Old Smokey"
6. Gotham City villain
7. Spring bloom
8. Take away
9. Mexicali munchie
10. Puccini heroine
11. Game with a bar in the middle of the board
12. "I thought so!"
13. Pirate's potable
21. Toy football word
22. Early fruit fancier
25. Showstopper?
26. Olfactorily offensive
27. Man of the cloth
28. "Cats" showstopper
29. Aura
30. It's to jump for
31. Terrarium plant
34. Virgo's mo., mostly
35. Universal Chinese ideal
39. Rx units
41. Keep a stiff lower lip?
42. Sending packing
43. Mrs. Ernie Kovacs
44. Nearly alike
49. "Casablanca" café
50. Close shave
52. Dig this
53. It'll hold water
54. "Damn Yankees" siren
55. Library ID
56. Can't live without
57. Zane or Jane
58. First name at Gettysburg
59. Overpermissive

99

Precious and Few

Across

1 Build up, as a fortune
6 Humphrey's nickname
11 Hoover, notably
14 Erect
15 "The Boot"
16 Prenuptial agreement?
17 Ireland's nickname
19 "I ___ Rock"
20 Burger accompaniment
21 Street urchin
23 Goldsmith's word
26 Election day stuff
28 School
30 Over
31 Morning or night wear
32 Downtown features
34 Two, in Tegucigalpa
37 Secret meeting
39 Billboard chart-topper
40 Buffalo hockey player
42 Match part
43 Watch type
46 Behind
47 America, with "the"
49 Pakistan's largest city
51 European range
53 Figure
54 Party throwers
55 Former South African President P.W.
57 Finale
58 12/7/41 locale
64 Muckraker Tarbell
65 Like the walls of Harvard Yard
66 "Born on the Fourth of July" director
67 A little sun
68 Jocks' counterparts
69 Put a spell on

Down

1 Goon
2 The word, sometimes
3 Had
4 Comes up for air
5 Powerful ancient city-state
6 Pass, as time
7 Blues singer Redding
8 Service station stuff
9 Suffering
10 Monocle
11 Turtle variety
12 Let in
13 Complains
18 Shopping and laundry
22 Ring great
23 Breath mint brand
24 Love to pieces
25 Rolling Stones hit
26 Hungarian composer Béla
27 "The ___ of Innocence"
29 Patriot Allen and author Canin
33 "Texas tea"
35 Correct, in combinations
36 Greet at the door
38 Dramatic downturn
41 Pick-and-choose
44 Alphabet sequence
45 Wayne's "Wayne's World" pal
48 Rebellious Turner
50 Beat a dead horse
51 "A League of ___ Own"
52 Ford rival
55 Raised
56 Former Ford rival
59 Jan Brady portrayer ___ Plumb
60 Word on many planes
61 Moving-day burden
62 List starter
63 Communist

Anytown, USA

Across

1 Somewhat
5 Not cool
10 Cold War nation, for short
14 Work with cargo
15 Hangman's rope
16 TV's Dr. ___
17 Midwestern city of burglars?
19 Easily fooled people
20 Mountain mentioned in Genesis
21 "I'm just ___!"
23 Material for pantyhose
24 Files, like a complaint
27 Smallest in number
32 Make free from vermin, like the Pied Piper did
33 Funny line in a play
36 It can be lame
38 Money for the future
39 Street, on some New Orleans signs
40 Southern city of parodies?
41 8 1/2" x 11" paper size: abbr.
42 Suffix for Brooklyn
43 Choice
44 Circus crowd's sounds
45 Large string instrument
47 Jam or jelly
49 Food sources for whales
51 Throws parties
55 Sniffers
57 Scottish pattern
58 How some feel after espresso
60 New England city of class reunions?
63 General feeling
64 Shotgun measure
65 No longer green
66 Tattoo artist's supply
67 Finish with, as a high note
68 Practice boxing

Down

1 "Wozzeck" composer Berg
2 Humorist Dave
3 Perfect
4 Rip loose, like a coupon
5 Apartment, to a renter
6 ___-smoking section
7 Take all of, like the covers
8 Egyptian goddess
9 Kind of code
10 Good part of the deal
11 Southern city that's utopian?
12 Have a bit of, as brandy
13 "Treasure Island" author's initials
18 "Citizen ___"
22 Sing from the hills
25 Your planet
26 American or Australian flag features
28 Show sorrow
29 Ways off the highway
30 Kind of money
31 Henry VIII's house
33 Masonry block
34 Word before space or limits
35 Midwestern city of average health?
37 Not nuts
40 Shearer's products
44 Groupies
46 Famed insurer
48 Monomaniacal captain of literature
50 Twilled fabric
52 Comics page feature
53 Florida city
54 Villain's look
56 Actor Penn
57 U.S. Treasury agents
58 Big music publisher
59 Cheadle or King
61 Dirt plus water
62 It may get stroked

Models

Across

1 Expert
4 Single or double
11 Rd. crossers
14 Not strict
15 Part of USA
16 Kitchen floor tool
17 Late model who had a hit reality show
20 Burn
21 Tricycle rider
22 Bakery product
23 Sister of Moses
25 Baseball player who played the dad on "Mr. Belvedere"
26 Throw in
27 Store with fashionable ads, with "The"
29 Vinyl spinners
30 Dander
31 Supplies oxygen to
33 Gets a look at
34 Model who guest hosted on "Regis & Kathie Lee"
37 Go off on a tangent
38 Holy Roman Empire rulers
39 www.tulane.___
40 Holds
41 Prefix for center
42 1960s campus org.
45 Smith's crayon-making partner
47 Concert memento
49 Village leader
50 Shade
53 Nairobi's nation
54 Model once engaged to David Copperfield
57 Meowing pet
58 Morally right
59 Take advantage of
60 Blackjack half
61 Actor Brian of "F/X" and "Tommy Boy"
62 Inc., in England

Down

1 Blood part
2 Like butter left out too long
3 City in Ventura County, Calif.
4 Wrapped up
5 "What ___ saying?"
6 Religious offshoot
7 Ending for switch
8 Sword's handle
9 Winter hazard
10 Preferences
11 With a more smug smile
12 Walked unsteadily
13 Areas
18 Boxer played by Will Smith
19 Leather shoe, for short
24 Name in cosmetics sales
25 Like some hair
28 Rodents of South America
29 Apartment agreement?
31 Word with red or army
32 Prefix with angle
33 Sea plea
34 Nice car
35 Overwhelm
36 In a playful manner
37 Only Hitchcock film to win Best Picture
40 Gathered (together)
42 Like decadent desserts
43 Most arid
44 Looked in awe
46 Original, in Oberammergau
48 Magazine magnate, familiarly
50 Los Angeles mayor, 2001-2005
51 "...will smile and take ___" (Steve Winwood lyric)
52 "Behold," to Caesar
55 Mineral suffix
56 "I told you so!" laugh

Essay Test

Across

1 She played Gretchen on "Benson"
5 Military alert status
11 One of a one-two
14 Oil or gas
15 Fighting ___ (Big Ten team)
16 Fifth word of the Gettysburg Address
17 Where to prepare
19 Tight spot
20 "Hamlet" fop
21 1999 AT&T purchase
22 Hardy cabbage
23 Reticent Romeo
27 Scaredy-cat player of 1939
29 "Hold On Tight" rockers
30 Prodigy rival, familiarly
31 St. Bernards' beat
34 Watts happening?
38 J.J. Pershing's command in WWI
39 Cost-of-living no.
40 Tempe sch.
42 "Inside the NFL" cable channel
43 "Four" at the fore
45 Oomph
48 Rover's remark
50 Here-there connector
51 First to be counted
52 Childhood "friend"
57 Egyptian Christian
58 ___ de plume
59 World revolution?
62 Initials, perhaps
63 It may give you ten minutes more
66 Potash
67 "Marnie" star Tippi
68 Salinger girl
69 Morse morsel
70 Parisian palace
71 Torvill's skating partner

Down

1 Choice words
2 Enthusiasts
3 Engaging device
4 Kasbah setting
5 Cacophony
6 Taina of "The 39 Steps"
7 Aircraft carrier
8 Roughly
9 New York silverware city
10 Long of "Boyz N the Hood"
11 "Aladdin" genie
12 Spry
13 Rocky Balboa, for one
18 Truckers' watchdog: abbr.
22 Drug unit
24 Cut the mustard?
25 Island in New York Harbor
26 Do a swab job
27 Future atty.'s exam
28 "Just ___ bit"
32 Nape drape
33 One who knew the Angles
35 It'll always be long in a limo
36 Longtime Israeli diplomat
37 Poly preceder
41 Raipur wrap
44 Rapids transit?
46 Captivates
47 Beaded, perhaps
49 Herb that tastes like licorice
52 Chew out
53 ___ Rose (Axis Sally's counterpart)
54 Bent out of shape
55 TV puppet surname
56 Kiwi's late kin
60 "The Joy of Cooking" author Rombauer
61 Revenuers, for short
63 George Sand or George Eliot, really
64 Snore?
65 Toronto-to-Montreal dir.

Staff Party

Across

1 Stylish
7 Water, facetiously
15 Quote by rote
16 Backslid
17 Battery terminals
18 Start up
19 Muscle car, perhaps
21 Do some meadow munching
22 Puff the Magic Dragon's home
23 Birthday attire?
25 "___ la Douce"
27 Annoy
31 Nonchalant
35 Kinky coif
37 Rover's reward
38 Small stream
39 Mythical giant
40 Timber tool
41 Rick's old flame
42 What little things mean
43 Small stream
44 Like Mr. Magoo
46 Radar's favorite pop
48 Industrial-strength air?
50 Sirius, or Lassie
55 Chalkboard
58 Top of the world
60 '73 Hoffman-McQueen flick
62 Intensely passionate
63 Amusing tale
64 Rubbed off
65 Primitive time
66 Cleopatra's love

Down

1 Kind of dive or diet
2 Slowly, to Solti
3 Oak, in a nutshell
4 The hit on a 45, usually
5 Shooting marble
6 Day or year beginning
7 Jason's craft
8 Exploits
9 PC key
10 The youngest Simpson
11 Beers and cheers setting
12 Three oceans touch it
13 Kay of "Rich Man, Poor Man"
14 Competitive advantage
20 Return to sender, e.g.
24 Chance ___ (happen to meet)
26 Burns' "sweet" stream
28 Rowdydow
29 Auto maker Ferrari
30 Smell awful
31 Fedora feature
32 Comic Tomlin
33 To boot
34 Sight gags, e.g.
36 For mature audiences
39 Dinner Bell?
43 Little ___ (Custer's last stand)
45 She filled a lot of shoes
47 Chinese restaurant freebie
49 Thou
51 Dieter of rhyme
52 Midsection
53 Out of this world
54 "I Am Woman" singer Helen
55 Surveyor's nail
56 Lang of Smallville
57 Copycat
59 Washington bills
61 Bump locale

The Fab Four Times Two

Across

1 Cold money
5 Wore
10 Mideastern menaces
14 Felipe of baseball
15 Wagner specialty
16 Only Huxtable boy
17 Some citrus
19 Cafeteria need
20 Beatles song about their apparent favorite number
22 Perfect score, often
23 Bus. "pay me" notice
24 Beliefs
28 ___ choice (baseball play)
33 Plot of land
34 Arm bones
35 Luau dish
36 Beatles song about the square of their number
40 Pitcher's stat
41 Argon and krypton
42 Provoke
43 Oregon Trail folk
45 Covers with soil
47 Part of many Brazilian place names
48 USNA rank
49 Another Beatles song about their number
57 Horse's gait
58 Introvert, perhaps
59 Latin for "I forbid"
60 Take time to enjoy
61 "Tickle-me" fad of '96
62 Explorer Hernando de ___
63 America, familiarly
64 Country star Jackson

Down

1 Blanchett of "The Aviator"
2 Jai ___
3 Number
4 Grant of "Love Actually"
5 Masses
6 Pertaining to bees
7 Say it isn't so
8 Mined materials
9 Shuttle creators
10 Make an appearance
11 Lousiana State Fair site
12 Mountain
13 Sauce in a wok
18 Singer James
21 Aviation pioneer Post
24 American Vice President, 1925-29
25 Dark yellow tint
26 "My heavens!"
27 Pops, for example
28 Pop-ups
29 "Need You Tonight" group
30 Break bread
31 Fairway neighbor
32 Begets
34 Nation disbanded in 1991
37 Hemispherical home
38 West of film
39 Cat's covering
44 Pirate feature, often
45 Mystery awards
46 Amo, amas, ___
48 Start of a Shakespeare title
49 Popular cookie
50 "Hey!"
51 Snowbird's state
52 Stash some cash
53 Perlman of "Cheers"
54 Ken, for example
55 Actress Samms
56 Light stuff
57 Tubes

Card Party

Across

1 Low- or no- follower
4 Cello elevator
11 Prone
14 Lively card game
15 Tall cupboard
16 It's a drag
17 Pointer
19 Bulldog
20 Hint at
21 Thunder Bay's prov.
22 Deighton of spy thrillers
23 Old war story
24 You can scratch with it
26 Retired Senator Sam
27 Pedal pusher
29 Work a cure
30 Monogram of Mason mysteries
31 Muffin stuff
32 Dapper
34 Tavern draw
36 National Guard center
39 One of the Ladds
40 X, to Xanthippe
43 Tackle a hurdle
44 Play makers?
45 Soak up
46 Mug makeover
49 Track tipsters
50 Holly Hunter in "The Piano"
51 "The Joy of Signing" subj.
52 Soup served with sour cream
54 Tennis tactic
55 He knows how to score extra points
57 It's a wrap
58 Land of do-gooders?
59 Vichy water
60 Dug in
61 Left the cocoon
62 JFK's predecessor

Down

1 Culinary style
2 Tree ring, for one
3 Sleeping accommodations
4 Burdened with duties
5 Samoyed syllables
6 Counterfeit: abbr.
7 Colleague of Bela and Boris
8 Stuff one's face
9 Castle of dancing
10 "Phooey!"
11 Artist's garret
12 Weasel family stinker
13 Sparkling
18 Popeye Doyle's prototype Eddie
24 Go-between
25 Norse god with iron gloves
27 Donnybrook
28 Buffoon
31 Winter-month syllable
32 The Red and the Dead
33 Lockup
34 Poop or scoop
35 Short-order letters
36 "Our Gang" sprout
37 Computer report
38 Ghastly
40 Made chicken noises
41 Fiery fellow
42 "No kidding!"
44 Fired up
45 Winter pear
47 Memory failure
48 The Five Pillars of ___
49 Group of three
52 Titanic mass
53 Steinbeck migrant
56 Race or pace follower

Mixology

Across

1 Put up, as a picture
5 Cat: Sp. (anagram of GOAT)
9 Champion skier Phil
14 Actor Sharif or Epps
15 Prepare a birthday present
16 How storybooks are read
17 Long-running PBS show
18 Poker stakes
19 Describes in words
20 Chess computer + thick directory?
23 More skilled
24 Cold
25 Take a chair
27 ___ in "Stephen"
28 News notices
32 Bop on the head
33 Hit, in olden times
34 Samuel on the Supreme Court
35 Source of wealth + source of mozzarella?
39 Snug as a bug in a rug
40 Seize
41 Award given by a cable sports station
42 Aziz of "Parks and Recreation"
44 They house engines, for short
47 Biblical verb ending
48 ___ standstill
49 Kind of terrier
51 Colorful bubbly + Dallas Mavericks shooting guard?
56 Financial capital on the Arabian Peninsula
57 It flows from a volcano
58 Fig. on a car sticker
59 Insts. of higher learning
60 Corporate honcho
61 Take ___ from (learn something)
62 Gives the thumbs-up to
63 Benedict of "The A-Team"
64 His ___ (cribbage term; anagram of SNOB)

Down

1 Some Japanese cars
2 Microscopic organism
3 Bellybuttons
4 Fruit used to make wine
5 Metal band known for its foam costumes (hidden in LONGWARD)
6 Duncan appointed to the Obama cabinet
7 "Damages" actor Donovan
8 Gift giver's command
9 Peninsula in SE Asia
10 Sacha Baron Cohen character
11 It's reached after returning from a long journey
12 Meets by chance
13 Asner and Bradley
21 Music award
22 Not Macs
26 Ring decision
29 Lucy of "Elementary"
30 Airport abbr.
31 Picture puzzle
32 Put your hands together
33 "Ghost Hunters" network
34 Continent with Cairo and Cape Town
35 Genre for Talking Heads and Killing Joke
36 Class including salamanders and toads
37 Olympics chant
38 Teddy bear exterior
39 Average grade
42 Cash dispenser
43 Used a hammer
44 Total disaster
45 Marinade alternative
46 Website to see if your favorite urban legend is really true
48 "Prelude to ___"
50 Jordan's capital
52 Army's football rival
53 Skirt length
54 Completed
55 Bag for potatoes
56 Twosome

Pass/Fail

Across

1 Created
5 Trendsetting
8 Wife of the late Steve Irwin, a.k.a. "The Crocodile Hunter" (hidden in LOBSTER RICE)
13 Bed size
14 ___ the crack of dawn
16 Sprinter ___ Bolt
17 Three-piece suit part
18 Rogen of "The Guilt Trip"
19 Gullible
20 Lottery ticket that's also a coupon?
23 Person who vilifies ad writers?
24 Put money on the line
25 Dr.'s org.
26 Abbr. at the bottom of a letter
27 Airline whose last flight was in 2001
28 The Magic, on scoreboards
29 Enticed
31 Enemy
32 Go back and forth
33 The purpose of milk, in the mind of a cat?
37 Bushy-bearded natural health expert Andrew
40 Landscaping stuff
41 "Animal House" college
45 "Wow," in shorthand
46 "___ for Alibi" (Sue Grafton mystery)
47 Singer Bachman (hidden in METALLIC)
49 King Kong, for one
50 Memorial designer Maya ___
51 Grabbed the end of Indiana Jones's weapon?
54 What your card says when Toronto's NBA team sends you a present?
56 Home out in the woods
57 Where flour is made
58 DC baseball team
60 In ___ (like a baby, before being born)
61 "On the Waterfront" director Kazan
62 About 2.2 pounds, for short
63 Underneath
64 Make eggs
65 Once more

Down

1 "Jersey Shore" network
2 Totally great
3 Rotating power tool part
4 Diary writing
5 Anjelica of "The Royal Tenenbaums"
6 Old treatment for poisoning
7 Trails
8 Arctic expanse
9 Those things, in Tijuana
10 Colorful arc seen after a storm
11 Monaco's region
12 How bunglers operate
15 "Oh yeah, I forgot there was another one"
21 Fail to be
22 Staircase post
23 Most populous state, in college nicknames
30 Sesame, olive or canola
31 Co. that delivers roses
32 Weekend retreat
34 1990 NBA Finals MVP ___ Thomas
35 "What're ya gonna do about it?"
36 Key for Elgar's Symphony No. 1
37 New member of the pack
38 Qatar, for one
39 Award bestowed by the Annals of Improbable Research
42 38-down neighbor
43 Letter
44 Salesperson
46 Urgent infomercial line
47 Muse of comedy
48 During leisure time
52 Bar & ___ (kind of restaurant)
53 Willy ___ (candy maker of fiction)
55 Surrealist Joan
59 Female pig

Buy One, Get One Free

Across

1 Mosque officials (anagram of SAMMI)
6 Action word
10 24-hour bank features
14 Shout before a game of tag
15 Olympic figure skater Kulik (hidden in FAMILIAR)
16 Trade
17 Having a pair of purposes
19 Drumming great Puente
20 Immigrant's class, briefly
21 Horse with whitish hairs
22 Mineral used in sandpaper
24 Sugar alternative in chewing gum
26 Block, as a river
27 Doggie's doc
28 Where press releases arrive
31 Ravi Shankar's instrument
34 ___ bean (source of chocolate)
35 One of Tarzan's pals
36 It's smaller than a city
37 Hard to see through
38 Play like a bad CD
39 Judge Lance ___ of the OJ Trial
40 Frivolous decisions
41 "It ___ a big deal"
42 Hairstyles named for a rodent
44 2013 Golden Globes cohost Tina
45 Say without saying
46 It opens many doors
50 Bitter end
52 Cafe au ___
53 Lofty poem
54 Not closed
55 Increase the bet, in Vegas
58 South American country whose capital is Lima
59 "Need You Tonight" band
60 ___ in the bud
61 Overly emphatic assent said with a fist pump
62 Nair competitor
63 "Strawberry Wine" singer Carter

Down

1 Back-of-the-textbook section
2 Shy and quiet
3 In any way
4 Alternative to gov, edu or com
5 Word before pistol or kit
6 Totally necessary
7 Tiger's ex
8 2016 Olympics city
9 Type and type and type
10 Samba singer ___ Gilberto (hidden in LEAST RUDE)
11 Mysterious 1990s show
12 Win at chess
13 Dalmatian feature
18 Cantankerous guy
23 "I ___ over this..."
25 ___ the Terrible
26 Packs of cards
28 DEA figures: var.
29 Go around and around
30 Held onto
31 Prepare Kool-Aid
32 Greek vowel
33 Unfaithful types
34 One of the Three Stooges
37 Submitted a ballot, perhaps
38 Simon ___ (kids' game)
40 Trips around the racetrack
41 London entertainment district
43 Words at the start of a countdown
44 Get an F on, as a test
46 The P in PBR
47 King in the Super Mario Bros. series (anagram of OK, PAO)
48 Hubble of the Hubble Telescope
49 Gossip
50 Not quick to catch on: var.
51 Fencing sword
52 De ___ (expensive)
56 Between zero and two
57 Six-sided roller

It Takes a Village

Across

1 That is, to Nero
6 "All-American Girl" Margaret
9 Elite U.S. Navy squad
14 Alternative to a lighter
15 "Whadja say?"
16 2005 "Survivor" locale
17 Big book of stories
19 Sean of the "Lord of the Rings" series
20 He's always dropping dishes?
22 New ___ City
23 Huge Brit. lexicon (anagram of ODE)
24 Not fast
26 Nick at ___
29 "Sands of ___ Jima"
32 Dog or donkey
36 Ore-___ (tater tots brand)
37 Bedroom area that's useful to have around?
39 ___ Wafers (cookie brand)
41 ___ constrictor
42 Sci-fi author Asimov
43 He has a corny sense of humor?
46 Make a knot
47 Dutch beer
48 ID-assigning org.
49 Evans or Carnegie
50 Campfire entertainment
52 "___, four, six, eight, who do we appreciate?"
54 Fashion legend Christian ___
57 Guy who trimmed Dad's beard?
63 Texas A&M athlete
65 Doesn't lose it
66 Crosses (a river)
67 Cologne's continent: abbr.
68 A few extra pounds
69 Oak and elm
70 Make a tear
71 It follows either word in the four long answers

Down

1 Kind of Apple computer
2 Short name for Boone or Webster
3 Query to Brutus (hidden in STREET TUNES)
4 Joe ___ (average guy)
5 Not these
6 Ice cream flavor, for short
7 Actor Laurie or Grant
8 "I just remembered..."
9 Place to get your nails done
10 Simple victories
11 Chorus voice
12 Grizzly's hangout
13 Destroyed a ship
18 Actress/model/socialite ___ Hearst-Shaw (anagram of DAILY)
21 Griff and D's Public Enemy cohort
25 Recording studio sign
26 Japanese dressed in black
27 Turn of phrase
28 Speaks
30 Sports org. that includes the Liberty
31 Bad smells
33 Mazda model
34 "Garfield: ___ of Two Kitties"
35 School for French students
37 Salma ___ (actress who portrayed Frida Kahlo)
38 Thanksgiving sides
40 Biker's exit line
44 Toss, as a coin
45 Date on some food packaging
49 The back, in medical textbooks
51 Weapon often seen on "24"
53 Scary insects
54 Nutty
55 Conductor Stravinsky
56 Shrek, e.g.
58 Spittoon noise
59 Org. for seniors
60 "On & On" singer Erykah (anagram of DAUB)
61 MIT grad, maybe
62 Coral ___
64 Ending for heir or host

Follow My Lead

Across

1 "The A-Team" star
4 "Well, aren't you the fancy one?"
10 Indonesian resort island (anagram of BAIL)
14 Yes, in French
15 "Let me handle the situation"
16 Stratford-____-Avon
17 Mail order publications for those who make kids' sandwiches?
20 Surrounding glow
21 "The Iceman Cometh" playwright Eugene ____
22 "There will come ____..."
23 Cuba or Jamaica
25 Hockey legend Bobby
28 Go jogging
29 "The way I see it," online
30 "Consarn it, ye varmint!"
32 "I Spent My Summer Vacation Rolling a 300" and such?
35 Deli loaves
36 "What ____ can I say?"
37 "See ya"
40 New York Shakespeare Festival founder Joseph (hidden in CAMP APPLICATION)
43 About 2 stars for canned hipster beer?
48 Musical sequence
51 Car
52 Signal
53 India Pale ____
54 Passes into law
56 Early late show host Jack
57 Hyundai model
59 Person from Helsinki, e.g.
60 Reason to watch "Sesame Street" and "Nova" on mute?
65 Any minute now
66 Kind of off-road motorcycle racing (anagram of ROUND E)
67 "____ the ramparts..."
68 Pull on a tooth
69 N.Y congressman Anthony taken down by a scandal in 2011
70 Football scores: abbr.

Down

1 Floor cleaner
2 Bathtime sounds
3 San Diego neighbor
4 Italian currency, before the euro
5 Wilberforce University's affiliated denom.
6 Part of DJIA
7 How more and more old movies can be viewed
8 Late English princess
9 Show up to
10 Male cow
11 Words of regret
12 Captain's journal
13 Plug-____
18 Weep
19 Opera set in Egypt
22 1970s synthesizer brand (hidden in CARPENTER)
23 Rapscallions
24 Animals that get sheared
26 Wish you could take something back
27 Apt. ad stat
29 Different ending?
31 "Blast!"
33 Cartoon skunk ____ LePew
34 Walk like you're cool
38 ____ and crafts
39 "____ Te Ching"
40 Handheld device, for short
41 Big ISP, once
42 Keep slogging
44 Rum from Puerto Rico
45 "Sorry, you're on your own"
46 Full of subtlety
47 Berlin's country: abbr.
49 Department store section
50 When someone will be back, often
55 Make up (for)
56 As American as apple ____
58 Pigpen sound
59 Flower: Sp.
60 He had the first billion-view YouTube video (hidden in TOPSY-TURVY)
61 Squeezing serpent
62 Closest star to the earth
63 Wrath
64 Hosp. areas

No Theme Here

Across

1 Brick carrier (hidden in SHODDY)
4 1450, to Nero
8 Is acquainted with
13 Old health resorts
15 Gas checked for in home safety tests
16 Like bad lending
17 Tennis great ___ Agassi
18 Debate attack
19 Not true
20 Co. whose mascot is a dog named Nipper
21 Animal with antlers
22 Abbr. after a phone number
24 "___ Blues" ("White Album" song)
25 "Critique of Pure Reason" philosopher Immanuel ___
27 Sinatra song with many lines starting with "this time"
30 Point to
32 Kind of issues aggravated by gluten
36 Swelling (anagram of MEDEA)
37 Fall back, as the tide
39 Lisa of "Melrose Place" (anagram of RAN IN)
40 Actress Winona and others
42 Refused to go along with, like an idea
44 "If you asked me..." follow-up
46 Pastures
47 Soak (up)
50 "¿Que ___?" ("How's it going?" in Spanish)
51 Firework that doesn't go off
53 One of Santa's little helpers
54 Medicine man, hopefully
56 Con artist's cube
59 ___ 2600 (old game system)
60 Grocery store number
61 Doc in the field
62 Clean version of a song
63 Practical joke
64 In ___ (at heart)
65 1988 Dennis Quaid remake

Down

1 Lollipops and peppermints and such
2 Like acrobatic catches in football
3 She teamed with Eminem in 2000
4 "Waltzing ___"
5 Longtime newsman Walter ___
6 ___ straits (serious trouble)
7 Non-specialists
8 "Autobahn" group
9 Grandmother's nickname
10 In a strange way
11 Not better
12 Derisive look
13 More lively
14 No longer wild, as a horse
23 "The Mayor of Simpleton" band (hidden in NEXT CLASS)
26 "By the ___ Get to Phoenix"
28 Ryan or Boone
29 Architect Saarinen
31 Magician's opener, often
33 "Yessirree!"
34 "Falcon Crest" actress with the real last name Ortiz
35 Persian's paws
38 Scrape covers
41 Org. that gives out 9-digit IDs
43 It may clash with the rest of the suit
45 Draw
47 Lovable rascal
48 Not inner
49 "The Devil Wears ___"
52 ___-Provera
55 "___ Brockovich"
57 "Business Goes ___ Usual" (Roberta Flack song)
58 Scott who sued to end his own slavery

Ob Course

Across

1. Ladies sports org.
5. Beatle McCartney
9. Used as source material
14. 60 minutes
15. ___ Major (constellation)
16. Bored person's utterance
17. Thieves who take X-rated DVDs?
20. Cracklin' ___ Bran
21. Wound reminder
22. Chesapeake Bay creature
23. Quick drawing
25. Also
26. Tachometer stat
29. Not there
30. Company with orange-and-white trucks
33. Without clothing
34. Fascination with Dre, Eve and Wiz Khalifa?
37. Find out about
40. Fleur-de-___ (hidden in SILLY SEASON)
41. ___ Boingo
42. Jamaica or Puerto Rico, if you're drawing a map?
45. Bert who played the Cowardly Lion
46. Change the clock
47. Icicle spot
51. ___ lark (without planning ahead)
52. ___ Lingus (Irish carrier)
53. Way of doing things
55. Painter Chagall
57. Cheese that melts well
59. Part of TNT
60. Debt to ducts?
64. Wilkes-___, Penna.
65. Panetta or Trotsky
66. Duncan of the Obama Cabinet
67. One-for-one trades
68. ___ Tomb (solitaire game)
69. Ray of light

Down

1. Zooming noise
2. Like cookies made without ovens
3. Keaton of the Silent Era
4. Parabolic path
5. Add sparkle to
6. Part of town
7. Superpower that split up
8. Calif. newspaper
9. Spanish actress often seen on "The Love Boat"
10. Kansas county seat (hidden in VIOLATION)
11. Human organ
12. It's north of Afr.
13. Dungeons & Dragons game runners, for short
18. Keyboard key
19. School, in French
24. Extreme fright
25. Skirmish
27. ___-rock
28. "Tell ___ secrets..."
31. ___-than-thou
32. Seemingly endless pit
33. They usually weren't hits
35. ___ Taylor LOFT
36. Boy child
37. Track star Jones
38. Israeli statesman Abba
39. Moorish fortress in Spain
43. ___-Roman wrestling
44. @@@
48. Dress
49. "The Two Gentlemen of ___"
50. "8 Mile" rapper
52. French city where Van Gogh painted
54. Positive vote
56. Gp. for Baby Boomers
57. Hot wings cheese
58. Civil disturbance
60. Channel with the slogan "Very funny"
61. Labor org. based in Detroit
62. Sandwich that's now a potato chip flavor
63. Bar bill

What Is This?

Across

1 Spare ___ (barbecue food)
5 ___ in a lifetime opportunity
9 Picks a candidate
14 *Phrase once heard before a long beep on TV
16 Not a child
17 *Part of a memorable anti-drug commercial
18 Super ___ Bros. (video game)
19 ___ Landers (advice columnist)
20 Tavern
21 Scary snake
23 Unit of resistance
24 Relax your grip
26 *Cliche line from bank robbers
28 Furniture maker ___ Allen
31 Mentalist Geller
32 *Short poem by William Carlos Williams
36 Old anesthetic
40 St. Louis attraction
41 Brilliance (anagram of CLEAT)
43 Up to the task
44 "But you told me that..." retort
46 *1995 hit for Montell Jordan
48 One of a pair on the face
50 Windshield problem
51 *Game show intro
55 Like Boston accents, as it were
59 Fight club?
60 "A Beautiful Mind" director ___ Howard
61 Number cruncher busy in Apr.
63 "You dirty ___!"
64 Tabriz resident
66 *Dignified (but angry) complaint
69 Kenneth and Ashley
70 *Movie with the line "It's such a fine line between stupid and clever"
71 Make into law
72 Sea birds (hidden in WESTERN SUNSET)
73 Not daughters

Down

1 ___ flush (powerful poker hand)
2 "___ ear and out the other"
3 Dull
4 Leb. neighbor
5 ___ vez ("again," in Spanish)
6 Not far
7 TV series set in Las Vegas
8 Lab heaters (anagram of NEATS)
9 "Twilight" characters
10 ___ Mae Brown (Whoopi Goldberg's "Ghost" role)
11 "Dinosaur Hunter" in a Nintendo series (anagram of O KURT)
12 Former Secretary of State Root
13 Step all over
15 ___ & Costello (comedy duo)
22 "The Fifth Beatle" Sutcliffe
25 Start seeing a shrink
26 Comparison
27 Military school, with "The"
29 Farmer's tool
30 Writer Sholem ___ (hidden in HAS CHANGE)
32 ___ alai
33 Web address, for short
34 Chem., e.g.
35 Small ship
37 "Curb Your Enthusiasm" network
38 Quarterback Manning or inventor Whitney
39 No longer working: abbr.
42 Airline until 2001
45 Person who keeps a journal
47 List of mistakes
49 Paid athlete
51 Orange ___ (breakfast drink)
52 Actor Zac ___
53 Florida city (hidden in LOCAL ACT)
54 Enzyme that breaks down genetic material (anagram of DANES)
56 One of the Muses
57 "Cosmos" author Carl
58 Staircase parts
61 Penny, nickel or dime
62 Painful plays on words
65 Japanese computer company (hidden in PINE CONE)
67 "All Songs Considered" network
68 "Treasure Island" monogram

Hey Hey Hey

Across

1 In the best case scenario
7 Become droopy
10 Rooster
14 Nobel Prize winner Heaney
15 Vietnamese soup
16 Tennis legend Arthur
17 Belly laugh noise
18 Total: abbr.
19 Revolved
20 1990s children's show about how machines work
23 Close by
25 Country where the Taj Mahal is
26 Major time period
27 Anderson or Craven
28 Prof's helpers
30 Watch sneakily over
32 Naughty by Nature hit
37 "___ Karenina"
38 Light colors
39 Mounties' acronym
43 Former alternative to Twinkies
46 Unable to see
49 "The Heart ___ Lonely Hunter"
50 Little troublemaker
51 TV chef Martin ___
52 In the red
56 Letter-forming dance
58 With 63-across, game with marbles
61 Neighborhood
62 Wedding announcement word
63 See 58-across
67 Falsehoods
68 Part of USNA
69 Guiding principles
70 Officers from DC
71 Before
72 Wealthy crowd

Down

1 ___ Wednesday
2 Chamomile or Earl Grey
3 ___-jongg
4 Nebraska's largest city
5 President of Indonesia for over 30 years (anagram of RASH OUT)
6 Pre-1917 Russian ruler
7 Hall of Fame pitcher Warren
8 Sportscaster Rashad
9 Mob boss John
10 House in Honduras
11 Powerful bird
12 Cinnamon-covered snack
13 Like half of Obama's family
21 Criticize cleverly
22 "He ___ point, you know"
23 Ja's opposite
24 Sports channel
27 "___ happen?"
29 Phone downloads
31 Fire setter
33 Jim Bakker scandal figure Jessica ___
34 12 months old
35 Green light or thumbs-up
36 Blog feeds
40 Stylish
41 NYC institution
42 Sony handheld
44 Stench
45 Fun in the fall
46 Reduced ___ (cut 50%)
47 Hugh of "House"
48 Poor
53 Crossword puzzle inventor Arthur ___
54 "Did ___ you say that..."
55 Nine, in Spanish
57 Term of affection
59 Kyle of Tenacious D (anagram of SAGS)
60 Letters after F
64 Faux-___
65 Corrida shout
66 Fast plane, for short

That's a Tough One

Across

1 "Welcome Back, Kotter" star Kaplan
5 Unpleasant atmosphere
11 1980s TV star who hosted a reality show called "I Pity the Fool"
14 Wedding day vows
15 Anne ___ (one of Henry VIII's wives)
16 "___ the ramparts we watched..."
17 Five on a dude's foot?
19 Muhammad ___ (boxing great)
20 Passover dinner
21 "Put Your Head On My Shoulder" singer Paul
22 "Kilroy Was Here" band, or a mythical river
23 Tina of "30 Rock"
25 Black and white cookie
27 Words before "fire" or "emergency"
32 Friends, casually
35 Any minute now
36 Time off from the group?
40 Former NHL star Robitaille
41 Thorny trees
42 Co. whose mascot is Nipper
43 The right amount to be serendipitous?
45 Ernie's TV buddy
46 Herb that's also a woman's name
47 Old-school fastener at the roller disco
49 Not arms
52 Bread for a reuben
53 Madcap
56 Sitcom starring a singer
59 "The Devil Wears ___"
63 Vexation
64 Ad line that caused a Muppet to answer "You bet me do!"?
66 Turn down
67 More level
68 "So Big" author Ferber
69 Animal that meows
70 Nissan model
71 Awestruck response

Down

1 Band events
2 "For two," on sheet music
3 Woody's last name on "Cheers"
4 Miami Sound Machine surname
5 Two-year degree type (hidden in REMEMBER)
6 New Rochelle, New York college
7 Actor Tudyk of "Suburgatory"
8 Timex competitor
9 Birthday balloon material
10 Ques. counterpart
11 Water around a castle
12 Bank (on)
13 Cereal band with a rabbit mascot
18 You can dig 'em
22 Sweet and ___
24 "That smells horrible" reaction
26 Recessions
27 Spot in the water
28 Mad Libs category
29 Apres-ski drink
30 Spoken
31 Make it really clear?
33 Jeter at shortstop
34 "___ bleu!"
37 Candle end
38 Senegal's capital
39 Singer Perry
41 "A Death in the Family" playwright James
44 Like some truth
45 Party item with a tap
48 What this glue has
50 Where oranges are grown
51 Between six and eight
53 Stuff in lozenges
54 Opera song for one
55 "Same time ___ week"
57 Like paper clips
58 Computer brand (anagram of CARE)
60 Opera set in Egypt
61 Reading rooms
62 Letters that mean "quickly"
64 Primus leader Claypool
65 "... ___ mouse?"

Greetings Up Front

Across

1 Actor Estrada
5 Stir-fry cookers
9 Blue cartoon
14 Venetian barrier island
15 Cut text, say
16 Mexican mister
17 Nursery rhyme opener
20 Away from the shore
21 Mined-over matter?
22 Woman abducted by Hercules
23 Bauhaus artist Paul
25 Final Four org.
27 "Mayberry ___"
30 He raised Cain
32 Request
36 Eager cry
38 Car roof feature
40 Spanish mark
41 Where you might walk the dog
44 First letter, in Hebrew
45 Multinational money
46 Parched
47 Contact ___
49 Juices, with "up"
51 Away from NNE
52 Santa ___
54 Tightfitting
56 Other, in Oaxaca
59 Vegas opener
61 Vast amounts
65 "I can't explain it -- can you?"
68 Cyclist Armstrong
69 Bois de Boulogne, par exemple
70 Early Cosby show
71 Tourist's "must"
72 Egyptian cross
73 It runs in cold weather

Down

1 K-12, in publishing
2 Nothing: Fr.
3 Bucolic poem
4 Film company
5 United with
6 Peculiar
7 Metric unit
8 Severe in manner
9 Fed. support benefit
10 Press release packets
11 Computer "oops" command
12 Bread basket bun
13 Gratis
18 "To Live and Die ___"
19 Prefix with -gon
24 Wonderland tag line
26 Italian wine region
27 Shade of blue
28 Violin cutout
29 Respected elder
31 Take care of a spill
33 Bugs about the trash
34 Aromas
35 Make fresh again
37 Skipping game
39 Israel's Shimon
42 Singer with an Oscar
43 Primo
48 Kirk's helmsman
50 The like
53 Dweezil's surname
55 Welcome words to a hitchhiker
56 Mail carriers at Hogwarts
57 Asian cuisine
58 Pealed
60 Lake paddler
62 Facetious "I see"
63 Tot's down times
64 Eyelid woe
66 Collector's quest
67 Bother

You've Got Male

Across

1 Enormous
5 Lady's counterpart
9 Come to terms
14 Seed covering (anagram of LAIR)
15 Declare openly
16 Inside shots?
17 Chauffeured auto
18 Poodle name
19 Canvas supporter
20 Tiffany collectible?
23 Luster
24 Some explosives
25 Turkish titles
29 Vent, as a volcano
31 Clear soda
33 Fitting
36 "See ya, señor!"
39 Certain fisherman
40 What an air traffic controller sees over a stadium?
43 "Spider-Man" costar Willem
44 "Ditto!"
45 Doc bloc
46 Open, as a flag
48 New Zealander, informally
50 Gain offsetter
51 Salinger title name
54 Woodwork refinement
58 Training program for mallgoers?
61 In conflict
64 Entr'___ (hidden in IMPACTED)
65 Roman love god
66 Male duck
67 RN workplaces
68 Trig ratio
69 False friend
70 "The Rocky Horror Picture Show" poster pair
71 Crones

Down

1 They're decked with boughs of holly
2 Dickens character ___ Heep
3 "I want it now!"
4 Ties the knot in a hurry
5 Butcher's hook
6 They're made to take the blame
7 Hardly enjoyable
8 Between
9 One who cans?
10 It's neither black nor white
11 Coll. dorm bigwigs
12 CBS logo
13 Immigrant's study: abbr.
21 In theory
22 Letters in a ship's name
26 Comedian Radner
27 Mr. T's outfit
28 Missionary Junipero
30 Tokyo, formerly (hidden in REDONE)
32 Colonial era hairpiece
33 Singer Paula
34 Dallas suburb
35 Spats
37 Midwest tribe member
38 Boney James album of 2000
41 Eggplant dish
42 British record label
47 "Malcolm X" director
49 One way to pay
52 Slowpoke
53 Early 18th century year
55 Female demon (anagram of A MAIL)
56 Surrounded by
57 Belgian battle site
59 C. in C.
60 Capone's pursuer
61 Small, medium, or large: abbr.
62 Capote, to his friends
63 Gob of gum

It's Right In There

Across

1 Newspaper page for "think pieces"
5 Superlative suffix
9 Lined up
14 161, in old times
15 Henna user
16 Charge headlong toward
17 Alternative to glue
18 Daring circus performers
20 Quick fix in the shower stall?
22 Bible translation, e.g.: abbr.
23 Dearie
24 Thin layer
27 Lauder of cosmetics
29 Help in a heist
31 Geometry proof ender
32 Studied extensively at college, with "in"
35 Life magazine founder
36 Binary code, to most of us?
39 Tons
40 Like beatniks, often
41 ___ Lanka
42 Regrets
43 Shaver's need
47 Soil digger
49 Moo goo ___ pan
51 MPG rater
52 Advice to a lazy farmer?
56 Amenity at many hotels
58 Airline to Israel
59 Sedaka and Armstrong
60 Treater's phrase
61 Visit
62 Stand of trees
63 Bambi, for one
64 Thick soup

Down

1 Harmonious interval
2 Dishes
3 Sell outside the country
4 God, in France
5 State bordering Montana
6 Keep an ___ (watch closely)
7 Medieval worker
8 Subject involving sin, cos, and tan
9 Not sinking
10 Ancient Troy (anagram of I'M LIU)
11 Alluring aura
12 Devour
13 Some football positions: abbr.
19 Former TV executive Roone
21 Inexpensive
25 It holds your head
26 Ending for lemon or lime
28 TV award
29 Regions
30 Ernie's roommate
33 A jaguar might go for it
34 Plains native
35 Mother of Castor and Pollux
36 Author Caleb
37 Party mainstay
38 Fit again
39 Setting in most of AZ
42 Lounge
44 True believer
45 Morphine, e.g.
46 Was almost used up
48 Tweed fabrics
49 Garden figure
50 One who hears "You've got mail!"
53 Popular MP3 player
54 Zero
55 Rules, for short
56 Business mag
57 "The Matrix" hero

Letters to the Auditor

Across

1 Israeli airline
5 Poetic feet
10 Heckle
14 "___ Smile" (Hall & Oates song)
15 Regional plant life
16 Fencing sword
17 Low-lying island for VIPs?
19 Metallica drummer Ulrich
20 Way up a mountain
21 Was well-informed
23 It makes bread rise
24 "Charade" actress Hepburn
25 Really into debt?
30 Messy stack
34 Rosy-fingered dawn goddess
35 Excavate again
36 Egg white
38 Onion that is Georgia's official state vegetable
40 Wife of Hagar the Horrible
41 [not my error]
42 Chow ___
43 Line at a Manhattan taxi stand, perhaps?
47 Declares void, as a marriage
48 Recipe amts.
53 French white wine
56 Perfect place
57 Spumante source
58 Marine biologist?
60 Orderly
61 Navel type
62 Pilate's "Behold!"
63 High-strung
64 Russian rulers of old
65 Timetable, for short

Down

1 English assignment
2 Memory slip
3 Betel palm (hidden in SPARE CABLE)
4 Corset fasteners
5 "___ first you don't succeed ..."
6 100%
7 Layout sketches
8 "On the Waterfront" star Marlon
9 Writer known for Wimsey
10 Its members may pass a baton
11 "C'mon, be ___"
12 It's nothing, really
13 Lemon rind
18 Crazy about
22 Unearthly
24 Long, long time
26 Small
27 Not working
28 Widest numeral on some clock faces
29 Alaska's first governor (hidden in THE GANG)
30 Sound of amusement
31 Topo map stat
32 Competent
33 Combativeness
37 Word with Loa or Kea
38 Struggles
39 Postop stop
41 Thompson Seedless grape
44 Calls things off
45 Valuable chess pieces
46 Words from Caesar
49 Augurs
50 Mote
51 ___-nez glasses
52 Completely filled
53 Horse hair
54 Previously owned
55 Male deer
56 Colorado natives
59 British title

Wrap Session

Across

1 Multimodal, electrically
5 Mexican money
10 Rock's Jethro ___
14 Restaurateur Toots (hidden in GRASS HORSE)
15 "Pocketful of Miracles" director Frank
16 Cleveland's state
17 Records useful for an audit
19 Christmas
20 Tenets
21 Touring entertainment
23 Supplement
24 Torch user
25 Tailor's tool
29 Apple co-founder Steve
32 Baboon's big cousin
33 Arcturus, for example
35 Docs' org.
36 Banned insecticide
37 Student driver?
39 Pitcher's stat
40 Conn. institution of learning, informally
42 Bobby of hockey
43 IRS identifiers
44 Sweet strip
48 Through memorization
49 Occupied
53 Californian winds
56 Actor Keanu
57 "Star Trek" empath
58 Phrase heard after a chase
60 No longer working: abbr.
61 Overact
62 Look into a crystal ball
63 Except for
64 Drops into the mailbox
65 River of Belgium (hidden in GEYSERS)

Down

1 Animal lover's org.
2 Leafy green
3 Under sedation
4 End-of-movie listing
5 Pie chart amts.
6 Attention, metaphorically
7 "Don't bother explaining"
8 Baltimore athlete
9 Tea brand
10 Place to shop for kids
11 "Nope"
12 Stitch's caretaker
13 MGM co-founder
18 Columnist Barrett
22 School furnishings
24 Shed tears
26 Groovy flat?
27 AAA recommendations
28 Merit
29 Crested bird
30 Actor Sharif
31 Indonesian island
34 Coll. mentors
36 Former presidential nickname
37 Scottish hill
38 Footed vase
41 Period of decline
42 Stop sign shape
43 Benefit of merging companies
45 Gives a speech
46 Generic
47 God, to Gide
50 Eye parts
51 Capture
52 Chemical compound
53 Orch. section
54 Field of interest
55 Threat to a misbehaving child
56 Some deer
59 Pay stub abbr.

Hare Force

Across

1   On the ocean
5   Dunkable treat
10 Dating from
14 Fender flaw
15 Mrs. Gorbachev
16 Software "revert" command
17 Cordless vacuum brand name
19 Slave away
20 Fast-moving waves
21 Made furrows
23 Sugar suffix
24 Editor's piles: abbr.
25 Perch
26 ___ Paulo
27 Memphis's st.
28 Actress Charlotte
31 Bird feeder favorite
34 Atty.-wannabe's exam
36 Basketball position
38 Hefner publication
41 Racing family name
42 Lender's takeback
43 Hep to
44 Alley denizen
45 Adjuncts of 47-across
47 Surgery sites: abbr.
49 Become, eventually
51 Do-re-mi, in the major scale with no sharps or flats
52 Actor Kilmer
55 Life's work
57 It may elicit sympathy
59 "___ Good Men"
60 Comic strip venue
62 License plates
63 Skirt
64 Osso ___
65 Licentious revelry
66 Earnings
67 Close tightly

Down

1   Supplement
2   Kid-lit Dr. ___
3   Come after
4   Letter address abbr.
5   Gene Krupa specialty
6   Desert stopover
7   Tiny lice
8   Take advantage of
9   Sport fisher's catch
10 Cars
11 Chartered choo-choo to Chamonix, say
12 "Garfield" dog
13 Drop one's hand
18 Ole Miss rival
22 "Ars ___, vita brevis"
25 Put another hole in the maple
26 Eyelid woe
27 Busts broncos
29 Florence's river
30 Garden of ___
31 Cowboy boot attachment
32 Arm bone
33 It may have a roll on Sunday
35 Waffle topper
37 Israeli weapons
39 Groom's gal
40 Aloha and shalom
46 Restriction on some teens
48 Defendant, at times: abbr.
50 Full of dirt?
51 "___ Nast Traveler"
52 Fashion mag
53 Tropical palm
54 Popular disinfectant
55 "The Censor" of Rome
56 On the horizon, perhaps
57 Hosiery mishap
58 File folder features
61 Charlottesville sch.

Patchwork Patterns

Across

1 Send readers to another website
5 Russian pancakes
10 Slightly open
14 One of the Great Lakes
15 Caravan stopping points
16 Positive
17 Quilt block with fourfold symmetry
19 Swiss abstractionist painter
20 Hopelessness
21 Simple classes in school
23 Last number in a countdown
24 Delayed
26 Least valuable chess pieces
29 Dorm staff: abbr.
30 Nutty
33 "What ___ doing?"
34 Native American tribe
37 Tolkien inscription
38 One of the Bobbsey twins
39 2000 film that plays out of sequence
41 "The Crying Game" star
42 LAX data
44 Old phone company, figuratively
45 Asian holiday
46 Person who'll never get out
48 Part of a lowercase i
49 Roald and Arlene
51 Breathing room
53 Homes on wheels, for short
54 Picked up quickly
56 Gets ready for battle, in a way
60 T. ___ Price (investment firm)
61 Quilt block with fourfold symmetry
64 Imitator
65 French states
66 Escape clauses
67 Lat., Lith., and Ukr., once
68 Untrue
69 Wooden strip

Down

1 Salacious
2 "Dies ___"
3 Minor bones to pick
4 Retain in employment
5 "Changes" singer David
6 Cowardly Lion player Bert
7 British verb suffix
8 Wedding announcement word
9 Sea spot
10 Requests
11 Quilt block with fourfold symmetry
12 Section
13 "Cheers" actor Roger (anagram of SERE)
18 Kidnapper's demand
22 Apollo go-ahead
24 Regal attendant
25 Online newsgroup system
26 Collection of experts
27 Valuable viol (anagram of MIATA)
28 Quilt block with fourfold symmetry
29 Inn choice
31 Get ready to pop the question
32 "The Cap and Bells" poet
35 Religious sch.
36 Cardinals' letters
40 Famous London theater
43 Hiders' finders
47 Emeritus: abbr.
50 Houston team
52 Roused
53 Actress Rene
54 Nonsense syllables
55 "My bad!"
56 Some NCOs
57 Aretha's genre
58 Org. where love means nothing?
59 Attention getter
62 Skater Midori
63 ___ King Cole

Cross Words

Across

1 Tribe leader
6 Leg part
10 Married ladies of Spain: abbr.
14 Seek help from
15 Elec., for one
16 "___ Nagila"
17 Muppet in a trash can
18 Cry for help
19 Footnote abbr.
20 Cross (noun)
23 Gives kudos to
24 Hulled corn used in grits
25 Allow
28 Some chessmen: abbr.
29 One-named supermodel
30 PR concern
32 Zodiac sign
33 Mother of Zeus
37 Cross (verb)
41 U.K. native
42 Pooch
43 Wise words
44 Give off
46 Domino spot
48 Pod inhabitant
49 Punched by machine
52 Place for photos
54 Cross (adjective)
59 Skater Lipinski
60 Follow the cheerleader
61 Polish currency
62 She sheep
63 Folklore fiend
64 Frome of fiction
65 Actor Rogen
66 Executes
67 Unfettered

Down

1 Gator's kin
2 Sudden silence
3 Augmentation: abbr.
4 Cybercommerce
5 "... why hast thou ___ me?"
6 Valentine figures
7 Map book
8 Property claim
9 Spontaneous assembly often organized online
10 Shone fitfully
11 Torah teacher
12 Par ___ (by airmail)
13 "Alas ..."
21 Boy king
22 ___ Kippur
25 Arm or leg
26 Arab dignitary
27 Cab
29 Sinuous swimmer
31 Attend uninvited
32 Time delay
34 Big pile
35 Slight advantage
36 Between ports
38 Alaskan race
39 Clever remark (hidden in PROMOTED)
40 She had long hair
45 Very, in Veracruz
46 Dishes
47 "Son of," in Arabic names
49 Goes out with socially
50 Full of wonder
51 Wading bird
52 Love to pieces
53 Very, in Verona
55 Canceled, in NASA-speak
56 Start of a pirate's chant
57 Greek H's
58 Unit of force

Encore, Encore

Across

1 High points
6 Fifth Avenue retailer
10 eBay actions
14 Toot one's own horn
15 Notion
16 Foot or inch
17 Community of nuns
18 Song recorded by Johnny Cash in 1955
20 Musician's deg.
21 Curved molding
23 Mickey of "The Wrestler"
24 Song recorded by B2K and P. Diddy in 2003
27 Wide shoe size
28 Thurman of "Kill Bill"
29 Used to be
32 Sicilian volcano
35 Design detail, briefly
38 Explosive experiment (anagram of STENT)
40 Song recorded by Jackie Wilson in 1963
43 Spectrum maker
44 Tiny particle
45 Formerly, in olden days (anagram of REST)
46 Actor Brynner
47 Small shots
49 Mess up
51 Song recorded by Andrea True Connection in 1976
57 How a slob might leave his bed
60 Grammy winners Winehouse and Grant
61 Candy heart word
62 Song recorded by 'N Sync in 2000
64 Napoleon's fate
66 Tivoli's Villa d'___
67 Kick
68 Actual
69 Unlike a figment of your imagination
70 Late singer ___ James
71 Arena seating sections

Down

1 Manhattan Project goal, briefly
2 Greek island
3 "Dear Sir or ___:"
4 Ending for Japan
5 Kind of light
6 Command to an attack dog
7 Spot seller
8 Lock opener
9 Pelvic bone
10 Try to corner the market on
11 Upswing: abbr.
12 Scottish dagger
13 Eyelid problem
19 "Friends, ___, countrymen"
22 Take a stab
25 Reaches a maximum
26 British swaggerer
29 Have on (as clothing)
30 Makes inquiries
31 Let it be, editorially
32 TV athletic award
33 Drive-___ (restaurant window)
34 Hammer's target
36 Stage of development
37 Consume
39 Gas meter measure
41 Personify
42 Filing material
48 Pleasant wind
50 Bristle at
51 Roger and Dee's mother on "What's Happening!!"
52 Is forbidden to
53 Last of the Greek alphabet
54 Extra virgin ___ oil
55 King or president
56 2, 4, 6, 8, and so forth
57 Prefix meaning "extremely," in slangy constructions
58 Wall Street inits.
59 "I never ___ man I didn't like" (Will Rogers)
63 Smidgen
65 Top numeral on many a grandfather clock

125

What's in the Cards?

Across

1 Greek letter
4 Prevents, legally (anagram of PESTOS)
10 Three-handed card game
14 Photo ___
15 Chocolate treat with white sprinkles
16 One of four on a car
17 Antique auto
18 Hora, for example
20 It's a long story
22 Tallahassee sch.
23 Offstage areas
24 Dangerous exchange to be caught in
27 Bit of clowning
29 Don of the Eagles
30 Unspecified quantity
32 Ford flop
33 Timetable, briefly
35 Perfect score, sometimes
36 Ripple in a pond, for example
40 Yiddish "yuck" (hidden in SAFE HOUSE)
43 Formal agreement
44 Also, in Alsace
48 Zip by quickly
51 Lightly colored
52 Was nourished by
53 Starting point, metaphorically
56 War, in Weimar
58 PD alert
59 Civil-rights figure Parks
60 Court case standout
63 Actor Herbert of "The Pink Panther Strikes Again"
64 Florence's river
65 Comic Gilda
66 Part of a nest egg, for short
67 Unit of power
68 Result in
69 What Zener cards, which display the symbols at the starts of 18-, 24-, 36-, 53-, and 60-Across, are purported to test

Down

1 Expensive car
2 Used a toothpick on
3 Regular shapes
4 Computer key
5 Openly disdainful
6 Trunks of the body (anagram of RIOTS)
7 Happen
8 Crony
9 Emit forcefully, as a volcano does lava
10 Prefix meaning "tin" (anagram of ANTONS)
11 Egyptian ruler of long ago
12 Inverse trigonometric function
13 Casual shirt
19 Radius doubled: abbr.
21 Lots
25 Actress Ward
26 Bring to bear
28 UPS unit
31 "Much ___ About Nothing"
33 Acts as an usher
34 Popeyes rival
37 No. 2's
38 Hair removal brand
39 Radio feature
40 Fortissimo, in scores
41 Record label of Cee Lo Green
42 Curbside water source
45 Snitch
46 Gillette razors
47 Brainstorming sketch
49 Fictional detective Hercule ___
50 From the top
51 Word processing specification
54 Interview format
55 Flip over
57 Lassie
60 Tool with teeth
61 ___ kwon do
62 Packed theater sign

1

```
S W I M S   G I F T   B U B
O H M A N   I D A S   E H U D
P E P P E R J O C K   R A T E
H E S   A H O L E   F L U T E
      S K E E   F L A I L E D
S T A T U E   R E D O
O I L U P   P R O V O Z O N E
A V E   C L U N Y   R O S
R O G U E F O R T   P I C A S
      S L O P   A F R A M E
B O O H I S S   T R E K
A X M E N   D E I G N   F C C
I B A R   G O R D O N Z O L A
N O R I   O W I E   I O W A N
  W A N   O N E S   G O L D A
```

2

```
F I R M   C A L I C O   B O G
A R E A   A C E T I C   U R O
N A C L   A R A R A T   R I O
    E A R N E D Y O U R Q E D
I N D I A         S P Y I N G
Q U E S T S T A R   L E N T O
S I D E   N A D I N E   I E D
      H A R I C O T
O F F   A P I E C E   S O D A
B U I L D   Q U I L T T R I P
S C R E A M     R A I S E
C H E E S E Q R A T I N G
E S S   E N T I R E   D A N E
N I A   A L I S O N   I M U S
E A T   T O P E N D   N I N E
```

3

```
V O D K A S   S F C   F I S T
O V E R L Y   P A R F A I T S
N I N E O F   I B E E M I N E
A N T B U Y M E L O V E
G E E S   A D E L E   K A Y
E S D   P I T   E R M I N E
    M A N T A S   E D N A
C R I C K E T T O R I D E
D U A L   L E R N E R
O T T A W A   A S P   N B A
W E S   A N G S T   C O A L
    E L E N E A R W I G B Y
T I C K S M A N   H A G G I S
B A S E H I T S   E R N I E S
S L I D   A S E   A M A N D A
```

4

```
E M F   J A K O B   O R A L
L E O   T A C O M A   D A Z E
F L U K Y P A P E R   E T A S
  N U K E D F L A N D E R S
D R D R E   E K E   D I E
H O Y T   P A N T   W O M A N
L A O   R A G A   F A B
  D U K E C O D E R R I N G
    O W E   I M O K   E L M
T I B I A   P R O G   S W E E
E S A   R A E   R I S E R
J U K E D C L A M P E T T
A Z U L   I H E A R T N Y U K
N U L L   D A R N E D   L V I
O S A Y   S M O O T   E A T
```

5

```
R I A L T O   M A S I   F L O
O N L O A N   O F I T   R O W
D E F I N E C H I N A   E O N
E R A S   O A R   A L I E N S
O T S   E F T   S T I N G
    S T U T T E R C H A O S
H A B E A S   A A A   A M M O
A L E R T   A L L   K L E I N
S A N I   S C I   A T E S T S
H I J A C K H A M M E R
  A L L I E   G A L   A C H
J A M S U P   D M D   A T R A
E L I   N O P E T E A C H E R
D O N   K L U M   U T M O S T
I T S   Y E T I   S V E L T E
```

6

```
T E M P   P C T   T R A L A
R O M O   U H O H   V I P E R
I N I K A M O Z E   C F L A T
    E L A N   D E A L E R S
A C C R A   O W E N M E A N Y
T R A G I C   A L E E
T E R A   F U G U   R A N T O
H E R M I O N E G R A N G E R
E S S E N   A W E D   G A G A
    C U B A   S E R I A L
M O E H O W A R D   L Y O N S
A F R A M E S   I T E M
S P A S M   H E A D C O U N T
K O T T O   E R R S   B R I E
S P O O N   D A Y   S L A M
```

7

```
P E A   S A N Z   P O P P E D
I N V   A D I A   C R U I S E
N R A   P O C K E T B R E A D
D A T A   S H A Q   A L F I E
A G A S P   T R U   D I I
R E R E A D   I A T   N G O S
    A N I M A L R I G H T S
U B I   E D U   L A P   T O W
F A M I L Y G U Y D A D
O L A F   A G S   E D I B L E
  G O O   I S A   S A R A N
T H I R D   N T W T   L E N O
H U N G E R G A M E S   A D U
O L E O L E   T A X I   S A G
R U S T L E   E N T S   T U H
```

8

```
E G G S   A R C H B I S H O P
A L O T   R A Z O R B L A D E
T O Y O T A T A C O M A G O O
S P A R E   A R K S   T E R N
    M L S       E E N S Y
A O L   L O C A L A D
C H E V Y M A L I B U O Y E D
E S A I   U T I C A   R E L Y
H O N D A C I V I C T R O L A
    C H E E T A H   W A N
J A M I E       B E A
A M O N   T R A P   O S C A R
F O R D F I E S T A C C A T O
A V E R A G E O U T   A K O N
R E L A X E D F I T   P E P A
```

9

```
S R S   K A T O   S P A
L E W D   I C E D A M   W E T
A T E E   T H R O W A P A S S
  R E A L T Y P R E S E N C E
T I T L E S   S H A N I A
T E H E E   A D O U R
O V E R T H E H U M P T Y
P E R   O C O M E   O R A
  B E A U T Y B R I D G E S
    A R G O S   K R U S H
S N A T C H   H E A R T Y
W E G O T T H E B E A T T Y
E G G N O O D L E S   C C L I
D E I   S N A K E S   H U E D
E V E   Y O R E   P D S
```

10

```
S C E N E   ■   M A G N E T S
E R O T I C A   C A R I B O U
C A S H C O B   I S O T O P E
O S T   L U G     G E L I D
  A M A I Z E I N G R A C E
M I N O S   Z O O E Y
O O Z I E R   S N O   S T U D
S T A R C H Y   A N D H U S K
H A S A   E A T   S O I R E E
      W I R E D   H E N R Y
T H E W O N D E R E A R S
H A L A L   S I T     T E D
O G I L V I E   E H O M I N Y
R E S E E D S   D E V O L V E
O N A S S I S   L A C E Y
```

11

```
V O C A B   C D C   M A N G Y
A T O L L   O W L   I T A L O
L O U I E   P E A G R A V E L
  N C A A   E I N   L E N O
P E T E R G A B R I E L
A G T   Y I N   E P S   P A S
P R O M   R N A   A B O V O
P E T R O L E U M D I E S E L
A T E I N   F I E   E T R E
S S N   C I I   S L Y   A S I
  P E R F E C T A N G E L
A S I A   O O X   A M I E
P E R S O N N E L   A N D I E
P L A T H   L C D   H O U N D
S A N Y O   Y S L   A N E E D
```

12

```
L E T S B E   T H A   N S F W
O N E O U T   H I N   A U R A
A S S O R T   E D T   S M O G
D U S T J A C K E E I G H T
S E I     A N O T E   O R B
  S E V E N F O U R L A T E R
    O X O   T S O   L A N A
K P D U T Y     J A I L E D
E R I C   O A S   A R B
W I S H F U L T E N K I N G
L I U   A R L O S   L I A
  N I N E T W O I T S E L F
R E I D   N I A   S O M A L I
A N T E   O M G   A Y E S I R
G O Y A   T E E   T S E T S E
```

13

```
T R A C T O R P U L L   K E A
H O N E Y B O O B O O   A N D
E N G L I S H R O S E   Z O D
I C E I N     A T S T A K E
D O R A G S   I T I S S A I D
    I L E R   N E E
G E R O N I M O   A R T G U M
A L A R   P I N E D   S O N E
B I T M A P   S T A T E P E N
    O N E   O O Z E
S H E R I D A N   E N E S C U
C A K E M I X     O A T E S
A N I   I N T E L I N S I D E
R O N   S T O R E K E E P E R
F I G   M O N E Y O R D E R S
```

14

```
U S E M E   R A D O   M A J A
H O Y A S   O D E S   I R E S
F R E N C H C U F F   N O W S
  S L E E K L Y   N E M E A
P I T Y   N E T   G E R A L D
I R R   O R T   M E S A
L A A   F I S C A L C L I F F
A N I T A   L A Y   A S N E R
F I N I S H E D O F F   C E O
    M O O D   C I E   O D O
C Y B O R G   B L T   P S S T
H E A R T   M A I L O U T
E N T O   F U N N Y S T U F F
E T T U   A N D I   L I M B O
P A Y S   B O S C   O N E I N
```

15

```
S P E C   V A C L A V   E G G
C O A L   I G U A N A   M A R
A T T I C A A L V I N   P L O
T H A N E   S T E M   V E E S
M O W G L I   A C O R N S
A L A S   S T E L L A G O A L
N E Y   H O W D Y   P U R S Y
  L I K E I C A R E
S T E E D   A T R I A   F P A
T I M B E R K H A N   S A A B
R E P O S E   T I C K L Y
I R O N   C A M A   T H E O S
N N W   F O R E F R E E D O M
G E E   T I E R R A   M I K A
S Y R   S L A L O M   E T A L
```

16

```
B O V I N E   M K T   A G S
E L I N O R   L E A R   S R O
A G E I N G   E G R E S S E S
M A D T V   C O W A B U N G A
    A N N   H O L E
Z E B U L O N P I K E   M M D
E M E R I L   A T E   V A C A
S C A L D   T U E   G E R R Y
T E N S   B A L   S E E N I N
Y E S   Y A K A M A T R I B E
  F O R E   A D S
O X Y C O N T I N   U N F E D
A R M C H A I R   A P O L L O
T A I   O R M E   A T L A S T
S Y R   O D E   H O O V E S
```

17

```
I Q S   M A L I B U   R I O T
C U P   U N I S O N   I O W A
E A R W I N D R O W   C U E D
B L A I R     R O B E
A M I N   C B S   R I A T A
G S N   T H E H A N G R O V E
  B I O N I C   G O N E R
S C R A M   I N C   U N I O N
P H A S E   N E R O L I
F O R E S T G R U M P   B O Z
P A P U A   S E G   B O N O
  O P R Y     O L D E N
J O N I   M O R O N S T U C K
O X E N   A D I D A S   K A E
N Y E T   C A M E T O   E R R
```

18

```
J U M P   A M B I   P E A T
E N I D   R E E S E   R U T H
T I N F O I L H A T   O R N E
E X I S T   B R A I N F O O D
    E P A   C C C   V O O
Q A T A R I     I C I N G
V I R G I N F O R E S T S
C L I O   S Y L A R   R I O T
  L O O K I N F O R L O V E
A N O D E     D I S N E Y
S I B   U B U   O E D
S K I N F O L D S   G R O U P
I O T A   I N S I D E I N F O
G L E N   L A M E R   S C O T
N A S A   E V R Y   T E S S
```

19

C	H	A	M	P			H	A	L	F			T	I	L
U	M	B	E	R		D	A	L	A	I			A	R	I
B	O	B	R	O	P	I	N	E	S	S			K	A	L
A	S	A			V	E	G	A	S			H	Y	E	N	A
			J	O	T				I	R	O	N	I	C
S	T	E	A	K	S	M	I	N	N	O	W
T	W	I	C	E		A	D	A	G	E		M	I	A
O	I	N	K		G	I	A	D	A		H	E	R	B
W	T	S		D	E	L	H	I		I	O	N	I	C
		P	R	E	S	O	A	K	S	P	A	S	S
L	E	S	M	I	Z			I	R	E
A	G	A	S	P		C	E	S	T	A		E	T	S
N	Y	X		P	I	Z	Z	A	H	E	L	M	U	T
A	P	E		E	C	A	R	D		L	A	I	N	E
I	T	S		D	U	R	A		I	N	L	A	W

20

B	L	A	N	C		Q	E	D		D	A	V	I	D
M	A	R	I	O		U	S	A		E	N	E	R	O
X	W	I	N	G	T	I	P	S		G	A	T	O	R
			N	O	D			O	R	I	O	N
A	K	E	L	A	S		P	A	N	A	S	I	A	N
X	R	A	Y	C	H	A	R	L	E	S		N	G	O
E	S	P	N		R	E	L	O	S		G	E	M
			X	F	A	C	T	O	R	I	N
D	I	M		A	S	T	E	W		E	A	C	H
O	D	A		X	B	O	X	S	P	R	I	N	G	S
H	A	L	F	M	A	S	T		T	A	N	N	I	N
	H	W	O	O	D			D	U	Z
B	O	A	R	D		X	P	R	I	Z	E	P	I	G
M	E	R	G	E		T	H	E		I	R	I	N	A
I	S	E	E	M		C	O	W		E	R	N	S	T

21

M	O	S	E	Y		M	A	I	D	S			P	I	P
C	R	E	T	E		E	D	D	I	E			O	N	E
S	I	G	H	T	U	N	S	E	E	N			O	L	E
		R	A	I	N			S	T	A	P	L	E	R
C	O	E	N		T	A	S	T	E	T	E	S	T	S
H	A	G		A	R	L	O			R	E	D
I	R	A		S	U	D	A	N		R	A	S	P
L	E	T	S	K	E	E	P	I	N	T	O	U	C	H
I	D	E	A		R	I	L	E	S		T	R	A
		T	A	P		E	L	S	E		H	E	S
I	S	M	E	L	L	A	R	A	T		B	O	W	E
S	T	A	D	L	E	R			L	E	E	R
L	O	X		F	A	I	R	H	E	A	R	I	N	G
A	W	E		O	S	S	I	E		R	E	T	I	E
M	E	D		R	E	E	D	Y		S	T	Y	L	E

22

A	R	O	M	A		S	A	B	E			A	T	M	S
P	E	A	R	L		P	R	E	P			F	R	A	T
B	A	R	G	E		R	E	N	E			T	A	K	E
		O	C	E	A	N	S	E	L	E	V	E	N
R	I	C	O		G	N	A	T		A	R	E	S	O
R	O	A	D	H	O	G		E	A	T		L	D	S
S	O	R	B	O			N	I	L		T	W	O
		J	A	C	K	S	O	N	F	I	V	E
	B	A	R		O	U	T			A	D	A	P	T
B	U	C		T	I	P		A	D	M	I	R	E	R
A	S	K	M	E		P	A	L	M		N	Y	N	Y
C	H	I	C	A	G	O	S	E	V	E	N
K	I	N	G		U	S	S	R		G	E	T	U	P
E	D	G	E		M	E	E	T		G	R	I	M	E
R	O	S	E		S	S	T	S		O	S	C	A	R

23

M	A	S	S	E		S	U	A	V	E			G	A	P
A	S	P	I	N		I	S	L	A	M			H	M	O
G	H	I	R	A	R	D	E	L	L	I			E	O	S
O	E	R		M	I	S	D	O		L	I	T	R	E
O	N	E	S	E	C			F	E	I	N	T	E	D
			O	L	A	F	S		T	O	J	O
S	I	G	N	S		A	T	R	A		E	I	N	E
E	C	H	O		G	H	O	U	L		C	Z	A	R
W	E	A	R		I	D	O	L		S	T	E	M	S
			N	O	O	N		L	E	V	E	E
T	R	A	U	M	A	S			I	N	D	E	B	T
B	O	I	S	E		P	A	S	E	O		A	L	A
I	M	A		G	H	O	S	T	W	R	I	T	E	R
L	E	N		A	O	R	T	A		A	R	E	N	T
L	O	S		S	E	T	O	N		S	A	N	D	Y

24

B	A	T	M	A	N		E	C	T			H	T	M	L
A	R	E	O	L	E		M	A	R			O	R	S	O
T	I	S	S	U	E		C	R	A	B	L	E	G	S
E	S	L		M	R	B	E	L	V	E	D	E	R	E
S	E	A	M			Y	E	S	I	A	M
			I	G	O	R			S	T	E	E	P	S
A	S	T	R	O	D	O	M	E			L	A	O
T	H	E	A	D	D	A	M	S	F	A	M	I	L	Y
O	E	R			D	E	K	A	G	R	A	M	S
M	A	R	C	I	A			I	D	E	E
		A	N	T	H	E	M			D	O	P	E
W	H	O	S	T	H	E	B	O	S	S		L	A	S
O	U	T	P	L	A	Y	S		L	I	T	M	U	S
J	E	T	E		N	Y	E		O	T	O	O	L	E
O	D	O	R		D	A	N		B	E	N	S	O	N

25

S	A	J	A	K		G	A	L	A	S			H	A	N
A	S	O	N	E		L	L	A	M	A			E	G	O
T	H	E	A	R	T	O	F	W	A	R			A	I	M
			N	A	S	A			D	A	R	L	A
L	A	G	G	E	R	S		S	T	I	L	T	E	D
I	W	I	L	L		Y	E	M	E	N	I	S
D	A	N	I	S	H		L	O	P	E		A	G	E
D	R	A	B		I	M	A	G	E		A	F	A	R
Y	E	N		S	P	A	T		E	S	K	I	M	O
	D	E	I	T	I	E	S		T	I	R	E	D
O	C	T	A	G	O	N		C	H	I	N	E	S	E
B	R	O	T	H			P	O	U	R
E	O	N		T	O	W	E	R	B	R	I	D	G	E
S	C	I		E	R	A	S	E		E	R	I	E	S
E	S	C		D	E	N	T	S		D	A	M	E	S

26

S	A	N		R	E	G	A	L		S	L	U	M	P
O	L	E		E	R	A	T	O		T	A	R	O	T
D	V	I		D	R	U	M	C	I	R	C	L	E	S
O	I	L	S	E	E	D		I	B	E	T
I	N	D	E	E	D			M	E	A	S	L	Y
			I	A	M		R	A	H		P	I	Q	U	E
W	H	A	L	E	B	O	N	E	S		D	U	M	A
H	E	M		D	E	M	E	N	T	O		A	E	R
E	N	O	S		S	P	A	R	E	P	A	R	T	S
A	N	N	A	L		S	R	I		E	S	E
T	Y	D	B	O	L			S	N	I	D	E	R
		B	O	O	S		E	P	I	T	A	P	H
T	R	I	A	N	G	L	E	M	A	N		N	C	O
M	O	N	T	E		A	G	I	N	G		C	O	N
I	T	C	H	Y		W	O	R	K	S		E	T	E

27

E	D	D	I	E		C	O	B	R	A			F	G	H
L	E	E	L	A		U	G	L	I	S			A	R	A
I	N	N	E	R		C	L	A	S	S	I	C	A	L
J	U	S	T	L	I	K	E	H	E	A	V	E	N
A	D	E		S	N	O			M	E	L	D	S
H	E	R	D		T	O	P	I	C		S	I	M	I
			A	P	R		H	O	A	X		F	A	X
L	I	M	B	O	C	O	N	T	E	S	T	S
B	E	N		J	I	L	T			S	S	E
O	A	F	S		T	R	O	O	P		C	A	R	E
A	T	L	A	S			C	A	M		P	E	R
H	E	L	L	N	O	W	E	W	O	N	T	G	O
S	E	C	T	I	O	N	A	L		W	I	E	L	D
A	R	T		M	A	C	R	O		E	N	S	U	E
D	Y	S		S	H	E	E	T		R	A	T	E	S

28

```
MAYO LEWIS   LAM
UTAH IWANT JANE
NORM GETTO OUTS
INDIRA TORTURES
  MIMIC MILADY
SUBPOENA SEE
TSAR NUNS SOLOS
AERO TRITE FIDO
GRAVY ETAL TRIO
  EOS ELEPHANT
WARMUP LEVEE
ETHEREAL ARNOLD
IRON ASYET IDEA
RENT RHODE LOAD
DEE  SEUSS ERRS
```

29

```
TESS AREOLA DRS
OAHU SEXUAL OOP
FROZENPIZZA NSA
UNEASE TOE ERIC
   NERO SALINE
EVAN REA MACYS
CEREALANDMILK
OTT VICTIMS LPS
GRILLEDCHEESE
IDAHO ERA ASIA
RELENT SLUR
ISLE RST INLAWS
SEE CUPONOODLES
ERR HEADON OBIT
STY ARMORS MARS
```

30

```
OMAN OLA PICNIC
DANA FUN UNHURT
IRKS FINALFINER
ECLAIRS BLOC
ELMO PEU OKD
PGA PAPALPAPER
ION LDLS SIEGEL
NECCO SSN REEDY
ASHORE INST LGE
TOWELTOWER KES
ORB ERN NAVE
EGGO MOPNGLO
ADDLEADDER EGON
MOULIN USA CEDE
DOESNT HAS KRIS
```

31

```
HESHE RST HEAP
OTHER SHEA EXPO
WHOLEWHEAT ACTS
TERM HEART LUST
OLE CAL OATS
HALFBROTHERS
IMPOSE LISA YEA
REAPS JUG LOONY
ANN ALAS GONUTS
QUARTERHORSE
MUTT MAS APE
SCAM SLOAN ALEX
HOHO EIGHTHNOTE
OMAR ATRA ETHER
PATS TEE YEAST
```

32

```
OCTAL AFEW STAR
NIOBE KANE CUBE
ERNST EGGBARREL
URGE ELI BRANDY
PIANOBANK APT
TUB ALLEARS
OGRES SKYE BOA
SWEETSTEAMJELLY
HEP HAWK EPEES
ANTARES PEI
ILA HONORDRUM
OFLATE ZOO EENY
KAISERPAY IMAGE
ISAK GERE DICEY
ETNA OAKS OCHRE
```

33

```
RISES HAMS APSE
ABORT ALOU GOUP
SELMA LISP ELSA
CREAMOFTHECROP
AIM PUT ERR CEL
LANA TRE BEGONE
SPOUTS TEASE
PICKOFTHELITTER
STREW HAVANA
ASIDES NET TUSK
TAT LET NCR BAA
BELLEOFTHEBALL
MIRO SURE HANOI
PRIG AGEE ARGON
GDAY WHEN BRINE
```

34

```
SOCKO AGATHA BOP
SALEM DETAIN IVY
THENICETHING GAL
SUM NAPS STUMBLE
MOSTEL ELIA
ABOUTSTANDARDS
BLISS TBAR JOE
AIRS ISTHAT BOON
HST OCHO AAHED
THEREARESOMANY
PRES ANNUAL
CELESTE CORD ANT
OVA TOCHOOSEFROM
PIC ERHARD ULTRA
ALE SMORES SUSAN
```

35

```
ALI TRUNK SPELL
ZEN HANOI PIXIE
TNT ETHELWATERS
EYES HOLLY RCAS
CARPOOL NEO
MOLLYRINGWALD
CLAUDE ONEG BEA
HURTS YUK RENEW
ISR ADEN COWERS
PHYLLISDILLER
ATT BELLYUP
ABET KASEM LONE
SOPHIALOREN KIT
TWEET POINT UTA
ALERT STASH MEL
```

36

```
SAPS BLU EFFECT
TROT RMN TREVOR
AIRPLANE CAMERA
IST ANO MURK
RECORDPLAYER
IRIS EMUS END
ASTRA ZOOM CEO
WHISTLE CARHORN
RUE ELMO AANDE
YES GAIA OTRO
HEDGETRIMMER
ISON EAT IRA
INKPEN INTERCOM
SLEEVE TOE HADI
PAWSAT DRS OLES
```

37

```
A T N O ■ T B A R ■ S E L E S
B E A D ■ W I R E ■ U B O A T
B A U D R A T E H E P B U R N
O S S I E ■ T A U P E S ■ ■ ■
T E E T I M E ■ N P R ■ B Y U
T R A Y ■ U R L G A G A R I N
■ ■ ■ K O L A ■ R Y A N S ■ ■
■ K E N N Y L O G I N S ■ ■ ■
P R I M O ■ ■ A R I P ■ ■ ■ ■
L I N U X L E W I S ■ K R I S
O C D ■ V E X ■ F T M E A D E
■ T I V O L I ■ R E S I N ■ ■
E M A I L Y D I C K I N S O N
L A B E L ■ U S E D ■ A L M A
F R E R E ■ S A S S ■ N E S S
```

38

```
F E S S ■ E X E C ■ T I T A N
R A M P ■ R E N O ■ A S O N E
U S E R ■ A N T S ■ K R O N E
M Y L I P S A R E S E A L E D
P A T N A ■ O L L I E ■ ■ ■ ■
■ ■ G R A P P L E ■ L A T H
O L L Y O L L Y ■ E M I G R E
R U E ■ L A Y ■ A V A ■ E U R
Z A G R E B ■ O X E N F R E E
O U S E ■ A M N E S I A ■ ■ ■
■ D A M E S ■ A L L O T ■ ■
T H E C O A S T I S C L E A R
R I V E R ■ C A N E ■ F A K E
E V E N T ■ A G O G ■ O V E N
Y E N T A ■ L E N O ■ R E N T
```

39

```
S W A P ■ S O D A ■ C A M E L
P A I L ■ U R A L ■ A T A R I
A L D A ■ N E R O ■ B O X I N
S K A T E D O N T H I N I C E
■ ■ ■ O A R S ■ U N E ■ ■ ■ ■
D A I N T Y ■ G Y M S ■ G E M
O L D I E ■ T H A I ■ P O L O
D O E S N T H O L D W A T E R
G N A T ■ H O S E ■ A L I C E
E E L ■ P O U T ■ A G E N T S
■ ■ ■ T A R ■ A L E S ■ ■ ■
B L O W I N G O F F S T E A M
L E V I N ■ O D O R ■ I D L E
E V E N T ■ L I R E ■ N E I L
D I N E S ■ F E E D ■ E N D S
```

40

```
B I B S ■ B A L Z A C ■ J A G
I D L E ■ O T O O L E ■ E D U
N A T A L I E W O O D ■ R O E
■ ■ S I L A S ■ T I G E R S
S T E I N E M ■ N A M E S ■ ■
L A D D E R ■ H U N G R Y ■ ■
A L I E N ■ S O S O ■ R I G A
S I T ■ S O O N E R S ■ R A N
H A H A ■ F R E D ■ T R O U T
■ ■ B U F F E D ■ B R O N Z E
P L U T O ■ F L O S S E S ■ ■
H O N O R S ■ S L A N T ■ ■ ■
A S K ■ M I S T E R G R E E N
S E E ■ A T E A S E ■ U R G E
E R R ■ T E N T H S ■ M E O W
```

41

```
S E T S ■ S T O P ■ R O C K Y
P R O P ■ T O T O ■ A N N I E
I R S A G E N T S ■ J U N T A
R O C ■ A R I E T T A S ■ ■ ■
O R A N G E C R U S H ■ S E C
■ ■ ■ E G O ■ L A S C A L A
T R A W L ■ I B A R ■ O T I C
B U T T E R N U T S Q U A S H
I P S O ■ E S M E ■ U L N A E
R E E N A C T ■ S E E ■ ■ ■
D E A ■ M A I N S Q U E E Z E
■ A P P L I Q U E ■ L O X
I G I V E ■ L O U I S I A N A
F A V O R ■ E B A N ■ S T E M
S T Y N E ■ D E B T ■ H E S S
```

42

```
R I M ■ P E N T U P ■ A C T I
A G A ■ A R O U S E ■ B O R N
B U S H C A R T E R ■ S C A T
B A S I E ■ U R I S ■ A D E
I N O R D E R ■ S O L A C E R
S A N E ■ R U M ■ D E P O S E
■ ■ ■ F I N E ■ D E L I S ■
W A S H I N G T O N G R A N T
E T H E L ■ E D I E ■ ■ ■ ■
A T O L L S ■ R O N ■ W I S H
R E E L E C T ■ R O S A N N A
I S T ■ D O R M ■ T I T A N
E T R E ■ P I E R C E F O R D
S T E M ■ E A S E U P ■ T E E
T O E S ■ S L A V E S ■ O D D
```

43

```
B R A T ■ M O L E ■ M A C A W
E A T A ■ A C E R ■ A G A T E
A I R G U I T A R ■ C A S T E
D N A ■ N D A K ■ R A S H A D
■ ■ A P E ■ N U B S ■ ■ ■ ■
I M A G I N A R Y F R I E N D
S O R E N ■ T O Q U E ■ D E R
U T E S ■ M O D U S ■ M I R E
Z E N ■ T O M E I ■ S A N D S
U L T R A V I O L E T R A Y S
■ ■ E X E C ■ M A X ■ ■ ■ ■
S T O L I D ■ R A C Y ■ J A W
L E P E W ■ M I M E S R O P E
A R E N A ■ A L O E ■ O V E N
M I N T Y ■ N E S S ■ N E X T
```

44

```
D E S I ■ S U S H I ■ T A L C
E D E N ■ A N T O N ■ A R E A
T I N S E L T O W N ■ I G O R
A B D U L ■ O U I ■ A L O N E
C L E R I C ■ T E F L O N ■
H E R E T I C ■ I S R A E L
■ R E S O L E D ■ S U M O
J O N ■ S T R I K E R ■ T U X
R H E A ■ E N V E L O P ■ ■
S O O N E R ■ D I S H R A G
■ N O T N O W ■ S T R A T A
L L A M A ■ P E I ■ E A S T S
I O T A ■ L E A D E R S H I P
Z E A L ■ A R R O W ■ E L L E
A B L Y ■ G A Y L E ■ D Y A D
```

45

```
A B O M B ■ A S A P ■ P S S T
B A N T U ■ C A N T ■ I T E R
C R O S S W O R D S ■ E R N E
S E R ■ H E R D ■ E R I S A
■ ■ T E N N I S R A C K E T
G O T O L D ■ P U R E E ■ ■
E B O N ■ S P I E L ■ O T O
L O N G I S L A N D S O U N D
S E E ■ B L E S S ■ P T U I
■ I S S U E ■ A D E S T E
P I T T E R P A T T E R ■ ■
O G D E N ■ L I E N ■ M A T
A L O E ■ W H I T E N O I S E
C O W L ■ C U B A ■ I N N I E
H O N E ■ S H I N ■ S E D A N
```

46

```
R O S C O E ■ G A S P ■ M E D
A L P A C A ■ A B L E ■ A V E
W E L S H R A B B I T ■ T I S
B A I T S ■ L O A N ■ S A D E
A R C S ■ A I R ■ G O P H E R
R Y E ■ C U B ■ ■ S H A N T ■
■ ■ A U D I T ■ P I E R C E
S C O T T I S H T E R R I E R
C A N O E S ■ E R N I E ■ ■
O M E N S ■ ■ E D S ■ D A B
R E P A Y S ■ R N S ■ S I T E
S O I L ■ E P I C ■ L O F T S
E V E ■ I R I S H C O F F E E
S E C ■ D U N K ■ O R I E N T
E R E ■ A M E S ■ B E A R D S
```

47

```
A C T O R S ■ L O P S ■ S I P
C H O P I N ■ I R O N ■ A N A
E R O I C A ■ S A L A D B A R
T O K E E P M I L K F R O M ■
I N T ■ R B I ■ A U S T E N
C O O P ■ E S T E S ■ E S E
■ ■ I N A F O G ■ T R U S T
■ T U R N I N G S O U R ■
L H A S A ■ R E E K E D ■ ■
S A G ■ V E R D I ■ E A C H
U N T R U E ■ O P T ■ C O O
■ K E E P I T I N T H E C O W
D I A B O L I C ■ O R W E L L
R E M ■ N E M O ■ W E E P I E
U S S ■ E D E N ■ N E S T O R
```

48

```
U R G E ■ E V E S ■ G O L D A
P H I L ■ M O D E ■ A R I E S
R O B E ■ O W I E ■ M I T C H
O N S M I T E T R A I N E R ■
A D O ■ R E L ■ L E G R E E
R A N D I ■ L E C A R ■ A P P
■ ■ A N A ■ C D S ■ O T I S
■ P U T A S M O C K I N I T
U L N A ■ H A L ■ A S L ■ ■
M E I ■ S T R I P ■ A Y E R S
M A R I N O ■ U S A ■ M A A
■ S O L O N G S M U C K E R S
B U Y E R ■ R A P T ■ O R E S
P R A N K ■ A G E R ■ O G L E
S E L E S ■ D A D A ■ K E Y S
```

49

```
C O S T A S ■ P H D S ■ B L T
A R C A N A ■ R E A P ■ R A H
S P A C E K ■ A N T I D O T E
T H R O W I N T H E T O W E L
R A N ■ ■ A T O ■ ■ E N R Y
O N E M P T Y ■ U Z I ■ B A R
■ S O U ■ U S E D ■ A L E
■ P U L L T H E P L U G ■
A M I ■ A S O F ■ P E R ■
R E L ■ R A M ■ B O D E R E K
C L I P ■ J A Y ■ ■ E N O
H A N G U P O N E S P U R S
E N G A G I N G ■ P O O B A H
R I O ■ L E E R ■ A L L E G E
Y E N ■ I T S Y ■ S O O N E R
```

50

```
O N E P M ■ H A L A S ■ E S P
O P T I C ■ A M I S H ■ L O U
F R A N C ■ N U T S O ■ B U T
■ ■ T A L K S H O W H O S T
F E D O R A ■ T O R E A W A Y
I T O ■ T L C ■ T R I ■ ■
C H O W H O U N D ■ R E P S
H O N E Y ■ S I R ■ C D R O M
U S E D ■ P L O W H O R S E
■ G A R ■ P H I ■ E E L
B A K E S H O P ■ A M I D S T
W I N S L O W H O M E R ■
A D O ■ O D E O N ■ D E C A F
N E W ■ P E N N Y ■ I N A N E
A S S ■ E S S E X ■ N E R D Y
```

51

```
H U G H ■ I C E T ■ T H E A X
E C R U ■ A U R A ■ H E D G E
A L A S ■ G R O U P R A T E S
R A N S H O R T ■ L U V ■ ■
■ ■ D I E ■ Y I P E ■ E G G Y
S C R E W ■ C O A T T R E E
A H A S ■ G R A S S R O O T S
R A P ■ O R E ■ S E W ■ U S S
G R I M R E A P E R ■ A N T I
E L D O R A D O ■ A N D O R
S Y S T ■ T Y P E ■ P A R ■
■ ■ H O E ■ O V E R T U R E
G R E E N R I V E R ■ O L A V
P E A R L ■ R E N O ■ M E R E
A N T S Y ■ A R T S ■ Y S E R
```

52

```
B E T S ■ C R E M E ■ P O M E
A X E L ■ H E L I X ■ E V I L
N C A A ■ A N I S E ■ L E S S
J E S T P R O T E C T O R S
O L E ■ L O V E R ■ I T S O K
■ N A N A ■ S T A T U E
S L A I N ■ T U B A ■ A T M
W I T H A J E R R Y O N T O P
A M T ■ O D I E ■ G H E N T
B O E S K Y ■ N E L L ■ ■
S U S H I ■ P A D R E ■ J A G
■ S T A N D U P A N D J E E R
R I S K ■ A M P L E ■ O L G A
A N T E ■ D A L E S ■ S L I P
P E O N ■ A S Y E T ■ H O S E
```

53

```
G O T U P ■ M O A T ■ T S A R
A N I T A ■ A S I A ■ H A T E
L O S E S A T U R N ■ E L S E
■ ■ A C T ■ S K I R T E D
■ S H A D E S ■ A R O M A S
D U E L E D ■ T E R E S A
A G A I N ■ L A D D ■ E R I N
T A R ■ A M O N G S T ■ S L Y
A R T S ■ U R G E ■ E T H O S
■ H E N L E Y ■ G R I E V E
M A S C O T ■ C O R P S E
A N T O N I O ■ A T A ■ ■
I N O N ■ P L U T O C R A T S
M I N D ■ L A K E ■ E E R I E
S E E S ■ E V E R ■ S P E N T
```

54

```
U N C A P S ■ U S P S ■ I M P
H A R D I T ■ S C O P ■ N E O
F R E A K Y D E A K Y ■ D A P
■ R A G E ■ R U L E ■ P E T E
D O T E ■ H I P P Y D I P P Y
T W O S T E P ■ ■ R E T I E
S S R ■ R A P A ■ T I T H E S
■ W A V Y G R A V Y ■ ■
A D V I C E ■ R E N E ■ M D A
P R I D E ■ C E R T A I N
L O V E Y D O V E Y ■ A N D Y
U N I S ■ A R O D ■ S C O W
S I D ■ F L O W E R P O W E R
E S L ■ G E N E ■ T A M A L E
S H Y ■ S K O R ■ S N A R L Y
```

55

```
R O M E · M C C O Y · L E F T
A P E X · A L O N E · E R I E
S A N T A Y A N A S I A M B S
P L U R I B U S · C R A S H
· · A R E S · E V E N · ·
N A N C Y · F L I M S I E R
A B E T · J O J O B A · S A O
M A S S E U R O P E N I N G S
E S T · A N D R E S · M O L E
D E S I S T E D · R A T E S
· · N E A R · B A I L · ·
S M A L L · T O R T O I S E
M A K E S A F R I C A S S E E
U N I T · G O O S E · E T A L
T E N S · O P T E D · R O T S
```

56

```
L E B E C · G I F · S P A S
A C R I D · N A N A · T E L L
W H O S T H E M A N · I S L A
S O U · O A H U · T I N C A N
· H O W S I T H A N G I N G
S O A V E · · E S C · ·
E T H E R S · M R T · E R G O
W H A T S T H E B I G D E A L
N E S T · A O L · C A D D I E
· · O Y L · · M I E N S
W H E R E S T H E B E E F
A U R O R A · O N U P · I S O
D R A B · W H E N S L U N C H
E L S E · A I R E · A R E A S
D Y E D · Y D S · Y E S N O
```

57

```
L D L · L O P E S · T U N A
B E E F · A V E R T · W R E N
J A V A · N U R S E M A I D S
· D I C E D M U T T O N · ·
· · T I A · · S G A S
C O C O N U T · B L E S S E D
A D A R E · O G R E S · S N O
P I N Y · S Q U I D · M I D I
T O A · F A U S T · B A S I N
S U P R E M E · H E R R I N G
· S E A T · · M A G · ·
· · B A N A N A C U R R Y ·
M O B I L E H O M E · E Y E S
A L O E · R E N E E · T A T A
P E A S · O M E N S · N I X
```

58

```
S C A T · B O L T · A S P I C
T O B Y · U N I V · S T O N E
A M O K · M E G S · T R I A L
G I V E U P T H E C O A S T ·
E C O · G I O T T O · W O R M
· · O H N O · S O B · N A Y
A C T V · T N T · I D O N T
D A R E T O E A T A B E A C H
D R A N K · G U M · U K E S
L O S · O R K · T A D S ·
E L H I · N A B O R S · B O A
· I T S A S H O R E T H I N G
A N A I S · U N I T · A L T O
M A L T A · N E A T · F L A G
A S K I N · A R L O · T Y P O
```

59

```
G A T E · P S S T · A P R I L
O P R Y · U H O H · S H O V E
O P I E · L U R E · S E E Y A
F L A G R A N T F O U L · ·
F E L L A S · S T A M P A C T
· · A S K S · H E S T E R
C O N S P I C U O U S · A L Y
R O O S · A S P · A R L O
U M S · C O N S U M P T I O N
S P I R A L · S U E T · ·
T H R I L L E R · G R O T T O
· G L A R I N G E R R O R
L A R G O · A G E E · N A S A
A D I E U · S E A R · E C C L
G O O D S · E L L S · Y E A S
```

60

```
A T T A R · A H S · O P I U M
C H A R O · S O I · B E C K S
T O X I C · T H E P O G U E S
I R I S H B R O G U E S · ·
· · E E E · S E P · R I P
A T M · R A G · I C E A G E
R E A P · D O N A L L O G U E
I N T R O · T A C · I N L A W
O U T O F V O G U E · S A N E
S T E F F I · P Q R · N A E
O A R · O H S · U A R · ·
· K Y L I E M I N O G U E
R O G U E S H I P · C L O G S
A D O R N · A N A · H E E L S
P O T T S · T E A · O S S I E
```

61

```
C I C A D A S · I M B E D S
O N A D A R E · S C A R L E T
G I V E M E A · C E D I L L A
S T E P S O N · O B E S E L Y
· · T E L · S L E E T · ·
V O W · L A U N D R Y L I S T
O N A S · S F O · G E I S H A
D I V A S · O W L · S N A R L
K O E N I G · M O P · G A U L
A N D I L L S E T I T · C B S
· · T I E O N · C H G · ·
Y E S I C A N · S C O R E R S
A R I Z O N A · T O M U S I C
W I D E N E R · A L A B A M A
N E E D E D · B O S S I E R
```

62

```
J A I L · S P R · P L A N B
U N M A N · T A U · A U D I E
N I P P O N E S E · I M A G E
G T E · S A W T H E L I G H T
L A R S E N · A L L · N E T S
E L I A · · A H A · ·
G O O N S · T E S T Y · S C I
Y O U K N O W T H E D R I L L
M S S · A R O S E · E A S E L
· · M G D · · S T A N
C H E R · E E L · C O H E R E
H A M M E R P A N T S · R E S
A R B O R · O V E R L O A D S
I M E T A · X E D · O N C U E
M S D O S · Y R S · A T P S
```

63

```
M A R K · K O B E · Z E L I G
A L O E · O P E N · E V O K E
N O S E B L E E D · B E V E L
T H E N E A R F U T U R E · ·
L A U E R · E Y R E · M C Q
E S P · C S T · E A T H E R E
· Y E N T A · A I D E D
· R E G U L A R F E L L O W
W I N O S · F A B I O · ·
E N T R E E S · V W S · O M S
S K A · E L M O · M A R I A
· N U C L E A R F A M I L Y
A N G R Y · U N I O N B O S S
H E L G A · T I N Y · E L A N
S T E E N · H A G S · R E P O
```

64

```
R A P T · A L L · T I C T A C
P U R R · P O E · R O M A N O
G R E E N E G G S A N D H A M
· F E E · C O E D · R I C E ·
A L A · I R A · E E S · T I O
H U C K L E B E R R Y F I N N
O L E O · L I V · S N O · · ·
T U R V Y · N E G · C R A M P
· · I O R · R E M · C I A O ·
C A T C H E R I N T H E R Y E
O S H · O D E · E V A · S A M
O T R O · D I O R · H O P · ·
T H E F O U N T A I N H E A D
E M A I L S · I T D · N E V E
R A T T A T · S E A · O D I E
```

65

```
T I P S · M T S · · D U B Y A
A B A A · A A H · D E N I A L
S E W N · R O O K I E C O P S
T A N D Y · S W I V E L · · ·
E M B L E M · B A A · O K R A
· R O T I N I · C A N E R ·
S C O T · L I Z A R D K I N G
A R K · A L P · M E X · G E O
J O E Y B I S H O P · W H E N
A C R E S · · U S E N E T ·
K I S S · F U N · L E E R E D
· O R A N G E · S P I N E ·
D A I R Y Q U E E N · I D O L
A T O N E S · R N A · N E L L
M A N O S · S Y N · G R A S
```

66

```
· C O B B · I P S O · M A S K
U N I O N S H O P · O B O E
P O R C U P I N E Q U I L L
· T C B Y · O N E S T O P ·
C A C H E · P R O D S · ·
O D A S · S U S A N · A L P S
P O M · S O S A · S K O A L
P R E S I D E N T Q U A Y L E
E E R I E · D R U M · O L E
R E A L · P I Q U E · A L O P
· E A R N S · S C A R Y ·
S P O N S O R · A I N T ·
P A T C H W O R K Q U I L T
O B I E · S A T I S F I E D
T A S S · E D E N · F I G S
```

67

```
H A N S · F O P S · A G E N T
A L I T · I R A Q · M A M I E
L I V Y · E S A U · R I F L E
A B E L L F O R A D A N O ·
S I N E A D · B U D · R A N
· S L O T S · F I A S C O
S E C · A M O O N F O R T H E
I R A N · D U O · P E O N
M I S B E G O T T E N · R O D
O C T A N E · H E M I N
N A P · F L Y · B L A N C H
· A R O S E F O R E M I L Y
J U R O R · C O D A · A C E D
A N T I C · C R O C · T H A R
B O Y L E · H E R E · H E R A
```

68

```
W H O M · A B E T S · G Y R O
S A R I · M A C H U · Y E A R
W H O A · O C H R E · M A N E
· Y O U S H O U L D N T G O
I M P U G N S · O A S E S
K A L E L · O M I T S · ·
O N A D I E T W I T H T H E
N E T · M U N R O · E A T
· T A G L I N E Y O U H A V E
· O I L E R · N O D E S
S H O A L · A C C O R D S
N O T H I N G T O L O S E
A N T E · A W A R E · I S A Y
I D E A · D E L T A · E T T U
L A R D · A N E A R · R S V P
```

69

```
Y A Z · R I B A L D · S I A M
E S E · A D A G I O · I N C A
S H A R K S K I N J A C K E T
M E L E E · U N C O R K ·
· X E D · C L O N E
A B S · M U S T A C H E W A X
T O T S · S U E D E · A N N E
T O R E · T R A I L · V E N T
I M A N · E G R E T · E R I E
L E I S U R E S U I T · S E R
A R T U R · · C I D
· A S S U M E · M O V E R
C O L L A P S I B L E H A T S
B R E L · A S S A I L · M T V
S E X Y · T R E N D Y · P U P
```

70

```
H A H A · A D D E R · A L A N
I C E D · S U A V E · N I N E
S H E E P S E Y E S · D O N E
S E L L O U T S · H O R N E D
· A R M S · C A P E S ·
E X C I T E · B A P T I S M S
R E A D S · J A M E S · H U H
A N T E · G U L P S · G A R Y
S O S · D A L E Y · M O R A L
E N C L O S E S · B A S E L Y
· R O O M S · S U M S ·
P L A S M A · S P R A I N E D
R E D S · S N A I L S P A C E
O G L E · K A F K A · E N O S
M O E S · S W E E P · D A N K
```

71

```
G I L D · B A B A R · I T E M
O D O R · A L O N E · B A B E
D E N Y · D E L I S · E X E S
S A G · P A C E S E T T E R S
· E R I C · E N E · S T Y
H A V E A T I T · T N T
A B I T · O R E O · T R O O P
A U T O G R A P H H O U N D S
S T Y L E · N I N A · S T E S
· D I O · D O N E T H A T
S A L · C D S · D O S E
T W O P O I N T E R S · N A B
P A G E · S O R T A · J O V E
A K I N · T R I N I · A S I S
T E N T · S E G A L · B E D S
```

72

```
R O V E · V E D A · H A T S
O D I N · E R U P T · U H O H
W E D D I N G C E R E M O N Y
A T E · D U S K · O X E Y E
N O O D L E · M U I R ·
· P R E S C R I P T I O N S
O C H E R · L O G E S · P O E
B R O W · P O C U S · S P O T
I O N · S A U C E · M O O N S
T W E N T Y D O L L A R S
· A I D S · O N E I D A
P A U L I · C I A O · T O S
B U R G E R S A N D F R I E S
A N K H · T A S T E · B O R E
M Y S T · W H O D · I N S T
```

73

```
L A U D   F L O S S   E T C H
A N T E   A E I O U   S A R A
S T A M P C O L L E C T I O N
T S H I R T   Y O D A   L O G
      E O S     L Y O N S
L E T T E R C A R R I E R
A P R O N   A V I D   S M U G
M E A D   F R E T S   S A K E
P E N A   E C R U   A I D E D
    S T R E E T A D D R E S S
T Y P E O     L E D
O O O   U S S R   L L A M A S
P U S H T H E E N V E L O P E
A R E A   O L D I E   O P E N
Z E S T   P L O P S   T E X T
```

74

```
J E S T   P A N T S   N E I N
A L T O   O H A R E   O T T O
S T A N   S A L O N   U H O H
P O L I S H S A U S A G E
E R I C A     P O L A R I S
R O N   P E P P E R S T E A K
        V I A   O S A G E
L C D   P E A S O U P   L O W
I R A B U     T I M
P O T A T O S A L A D   S T U
S P E L U N K     U P T O N
    P O P C O R N S H R I M P
J U A N   A K E L A   I N T O
I S L E   L I N E N   S K I T
G A M Y   L E E R S   M O T S
```

75

```
S C A B   F A M E D   S W I T
P O L O   A L V A R   T H R U
F R A N K Z A P P A   R O A N
S E D A R I S   G R E A S E
    N A N   C A N O E
D I Z Z Y G I L L E S P I E
A R I A S   S E P T A   R N D
N I P S   D O M E S   A I D E
G N U   F I B E R   E P S O M
A P O L O A N T O N O H N O
    B U R R S   U N S
J O J O B A   S T U T T E R
E S A I   M I K E P I A Z Z A
E L M S   A M A N A   T A R P
P O S T   S A N D Y   E R A S
```

76

```
S T A B   F I R E   A B A T E
T O T E   O R A L   V A S E S
O D O R   R A G S   A S S E S
P O P T H E Q U E S T I O N
    A S I     T A L C
S A D I S T   C H E R   I S M
T R E N T   A L O E   E A T A
R O C K O F G I B R A L T A R
A M O S   R E N O   L I E G E
P A M   J O S E   P A S S E S
    P L U S     E R R
  C O U N T R Y B U M P K I N
H A S N T   O M E N   R I D E
O M E G A   A C R E   A L E X
C E D E S   M A T S   M O A T
```

77

```
B O S S   A B S   H E G E L
O R E O   G E O   T A M A R A
W E T S U I T S   A R M P I T
    A R T S O F S P E E C H
E G G   G A Y   E M I T
G A R N E T   A L A N   I B M
R O O F R E A D I N G   S O R
E L A L   L O N   W I T H
T E N   R A I S E W O R T H Y
S R S   E D G E   R H Y M E D
    D E A N   T E A   E R E
I N K I N G S H E A R S
D E N O T E   T A K E A W A Y
E L I D E S   T S E   V I N E
A L T E R   P E D   E N D S
```

78

```
A T I T   D E S I   G O O F F
R E S I D E N T S   A N N I E
O N I N Y E A R S   L E D G E
M O T H E R C O U R A G E
A R I A   T H E A X   P O O
      T A B   P Y L O N S
A B M   L E T S U P   A S I A
F E A R L E S S F O S D I C K
T A R A   R E T O R T   T E A
O N S P E C     T E K
N Y U   M A S H A   E L O I
    P R I N C E V A L I A N T
T R I A L   A R I M A T H E A
S O A M I   R O S E P E T A L
K E L S O   E N O S   L I L Y
```

79

```
M A R C   G H A N A   U P A T
U T A H   R E F E R   N E M O
M A M A   E R R O R   D R I P
  D A N N Y B O N A D U C E
    T A S     Y A L E
A M B E R   A V A   M Y N A H
G A R Y C O L E M A N   T S U
N O E S   D A R E R   A A H S
E R A   T O D D B R I D G E S
W I D T H   Y E A   T E E N Y
    C I A O     K E N
  D R E W B A R R Y M O R E
Y O U D   E M A I L   I O N S
E M M Y   S I N A I   D U D E
R O B E   E A G L E   S T O W
```

80

```
A P I S H   S H E A   S L O B
V O D K A   H U A C   H O B O
O S L I N   U S S R   A L E X
W H E N D O N K E Y S F L Y
    N I P S     L I T
E L A Y N E   S W I G   I S M
L A I D   N O T A C H A N C E
L I M I T   S E X   T A P E D
I N A P I G S E Y E   R U N E
S E T   G R A D   L I O T T A
    T E A     F I N N
O V E R M Y D E A D B O D Y
E V I L   M O O N   E U B I E
L A N E   E R I C   B R I A N
F L E X   R E N E   T R E S S
```

81

```
A N S E L   B O P S   C E S S
C A C A O   U H O H   O A T H
S T A R R   I N T O   A S E A
  O T H E L L O T W I S T E R
    A L O T   S Y S T O L E
O C H R E S     P A R
C O O T I E C A N D Y L A N D
H U M   I S D U E   N A Y
O P E R A T I O N B O G G L E
    S E N   O N E E A R
A R C A D E S   I N S O
S O R R Y M O U S E T R A P
I D E E   C U R L   A G L O W
D E E R   E L S E   G I M M E
E O N S   E S A S   E A S E S
```

82

```
P I C A S ■ A R A L ■ S L A V
I N U I T ■ S A R A ■ H E X A
K U B L A I K H A N ■ A X E S
E R A ■ R N S ■ B Y A M I L E
S E N S E D ■ ■ A L A N ■ ■ ■
■ ■ ■ K R I S S K R I N G L E
P O S Y ■ C I C A D A ■ T A X
A N T E S ■ T O Y ■ S W O R E
R C A ■ A N O R A K ■ I N K S
K E Y S T O N E K O P S ■ ■ ■
■ ■ ■ S E A N ■ ■ R I P O F F
G R O W N U P ■ M A C ■ L I E
L O V E ■ K E V I N K L I N E
U S E R ■ E L A N ■ L E V E L
E A R S ■ S E N D ■ E W E R S
```

83

```
S C A B ■ W I M P ■ G A D D A
H E R A ■ O H I O ■ O L I O S
I S A Y ■ R O N S ■ E D G E S
F A M O U S P O T A T O E S ■
T R I U N E ■ S I G H ■ R T E
Y E S ■ T O S ■ T O E N A I L
■ ■ ■ S I F T S ■ ■ A T M S ■
■ L I V E F R E E O R D I E ■
W E R E ■ ■ P A D U A ■ ■ ■ ■
E V I N C E S ■ T O N ■ I M O
D I S ■ A L O E ■ N E S T E D
■ T H E G O L D E N S T A T E
J A M I E ■ V I S E ■ A L I S
S T A R R ■ E T A L ■ G I N S
B E N E S ■ S H U L ■ G A G A
```

84

```
J E F F ■ A B B A ■ L E G I T
A L A I ■ F O E S ■ A Q A B A
G A R R ■ O W L S ■ J U L E P
■ M O S Q U I T O C O A S T ■
■ ■ ■ T E L E ■ C A L L ■ ■ ■
B R A N D O ■ P I L L ■ A S S
L A R A ■ F L E A M A R K E T
A D A M ■ O A T ■ ■ A I D A ■
D O B E A D O B E E ■ S T A R
E N S ■ M A K O ■ M U T A N T
■ ■ ■ I O W A ■ F E T A ■ ■ ■
■ R U F U S T F I R E F L Y ■
J A S O N ■ Y A N G ■ A I M S
A T I L T ■ O N C E ■ R A C E
B E A D S ■ U G H S ■ I M A X
```

85

```
L E V I ■ L E G O ■ D A B O
A T A D ■ H E A R D ■ O U R S
M A M A ■ A G R E E ■ G R I M
A L P H A M A L E S ■ G O T O
■ ■ I O N ■ L O C ■ B Y R O N
T A R ■ T H E B E T A B A N D
A S I F ■ A S E ■ I D A ■ ■ ■
U P C U R V E ■ S L U G G E R
■ ■ L O O ■ S H E ■ S I L O ■
G A M M A C A M E R A ■ N O D
O N A I R ■ M A L ■ C C R ■ ■
F E R N ■ D E L T A H O U S E
E M M A ■ E L L E N ■ A M P S
R I O T ■ P I E R S ■ S M U T
S A T E ■ P A Y S ■ T Y N E
```

86

```
T U P A C ■ H A T S ■ N S A
S C O U R ■ I B E T ■ O N U S
E L U D E ■ G E A R ■ T O R A
■ A R I A L H E M I N G W A Y
■ ■ E T A S ■ S P O U S E S ■
A F B ■ E N C L ■ S D I ■ ■ ■
B O L D ■ C O I N ■ E L V E S
C O U R I E R B I G S T I C K
S T R U M ■ E Y E R ■ Y E T I
■ ■ M O W ■ A T O M ■ W O N ■
L A W S U I T ■ Z W E I ■ ■ ■
I S H O T S A N S S E R I F ■
E T A L ■ E P I C ■ T O N E R
S I L O ■ S E T H ■ U N C L E
N E S ■ T R E E ■ P S A L M
```

87

```
B U M S ■ B E N J I ■ J E S T
A T O M ■ O L E A N ■ E T T U
M U T E ■ M I T C H ■ W H I M
B R E A D B A S K E T ■ E L M
I N T R O S ■ ■ R E A L L Y
■ ■ ■ L I G A M E N T ■ ■ ■
S P A R E T I R E ■ D E W E Y
N O T I ■ E B E R T ■ I A G O
L E A N N ■ B A Y W I N D O W
■ ■ ■ G O E S S L O W ■ ■ ■
B O W S E R ■ ■ B I A F R A
E V A ■ L O V E H A N D L E S
L A N A ■ T E X A S ■ L O G O
L T D S ■ I G I V E ■ I R A N
Y E A H ■ C A T E S ■ B A L E
```

88

```
S P A R ■ S L U R P S ■ H U G
L A M E ■ C A N O L A ■ A H A
I C E S ■ O I L C A N ■ N O G
V I N C E N T V A N G O G H ■
E N D U S E ■ ■ B R A D ■ ■
R O S E S ■ M B A ■ I H O P E
■ R O B E R T V A U G H N ■
R F D ■ R A I S E ■ ■ S I C
K U R T V O N N E G U T ■ ■
O M A H A ■ S K A ■ P A R K A
■ ■ M A U S ■ ■ W O N O U T
■ S A I N T V A L E N T I N E
W I T ■ T I E R O D ■ A L G A
A L I ■ E P I L O G ■ R E F S
X T C ■ D E N O T E ■ A D U E
```

89

```
A S I A ■ T Y N E ■ C H A R D
T H R U ■ W O O L ■ H O L E R
F O O D C O U R T ■ A B A S E
■ ■ ■ N I L S ■ O P P O S E D
C A C T I ■ A G R E E ■ K E G
I S H ■ V I D E O A R C A D E
T I E D ■ M I N ■ C O O ■ ■ ■
I N F O R M A T I O N D E S K
■ ■ ■ C H E ■ I S A ■ E T T U
P A R K I N G L O T S ■ H U R
A T E ■ A S H E N ■ A R E N T
S H A W N E E ■ A G A R ■ ■ ■
S E V E N ■ T E E N A G E R S
E N E R O ■ T E A K ■ A A H S
L A D E N ■ O K R A ■ S L O W
```

90

```
S L A N G ■ A G R A ■ S M U G
H I R E R ■ C R A M ■ C U R T
A T M M A C H I N E ■ O S L O
W H O O S H E S ■ L E T S ■ ■
N O R ■ P A S T H I S T O R Y
■ ■ E S C ■ ■ O A T ■ L E E
D E S I ■ H A L T ■ A N I M A
E X T R A A D D E D B O N U S
C U R E S ■ I S L E ■ G I S T
A D A ■ S S E ■ L P S ■ ■ ■
F E W I N N U M B E R ■ A G E
■ ■ D O S E ■ O U T O F G A S
C M O N ■ E N D R E S U L T S
M A G I ■ Z E A L ■ E M O T E
D I S C ■ E E L Y ■ S E W O N
```

91

```
A S C O T   N O V A   I M O K
S O U T H   F A I R Y T A L E
I N T H E A L T O G E T H E R
S I L E N T   L O W   L A N
A N O   C O R G I   F E T E
I L O S E   A U N A T U R E L
D A S H   P I R   P O T
  W E A R I N G A S M I L E
  R O E   L I E   L I N D
U N A D O R N E D   L E V A R
P O W S   E D S E L   E M I
E T A   A P E   D O O W O P
N A K E D A S A J A Y B I R D
D R E S S C O D E   D I R E R
S Y N C   K N O T   S E E D Y
```

92

```
A T T I C   I N T L   I M P S
C A I R O   M A R Y   M A L E
C O P E N H A G E N   P R O W
  S M O G   E X P E C T S
O C S   E R E   R E L I C
B R A I N S   S I S I   H O T
T A R S   E T O N   E R A S E
U N C L E   H A G   D I G I N
S K O A L   A P S O   L A R A
E S P   V A T S   P U L L I N
  H E E L S   S T P   L S T
B E A T S I T   A I D A
O L G A   S H A G C A R P E T
G L U T   T A D A   T A S T E
S A S S   S T A N   E L I D E
```

93

```
A K I T A   P E P U P   S P A
R A W L S   O Z O N E   A U X
C L O C K W O R K O R A N G E
H E N   F O R A Y   F I D E L
  N O R   A U D I T S
W A T E R M E L O N M A N
A N A T   R O U T E   I C Y
S K I   C H A P T E R   S E E
P A L   H O S E D   E T N A
  G R A P E S O F W R A T H
E L A I N E   A H A
S E T A T   C A I R O   A W E
T H E L E M O N D R O P K I D
E A R   R O N N Y   S H I N Y
S R S   S T E A L   H I N E S
```

94

```
R V S   S C A M   N O S O A P
I C U   I S E E   E U C L I D
T H E P E A R L F I S H E R S
E I D E R   B A N T U
S P E A R H E A D   B E A N
  S A U L   S T E L M O
E S C   B B S   E A R F U L
L A N D S C A P E A R T I S T
E R O I C A   Y U L   N E E
C A T N I P   R U S H
T H E O   F L O P E A R E D
  S U S I E   A I O L I
D I S A P P E A R I N G A C T
A S T U T E   C I N C   S A T
T H E R O D   H O K E   T R Y
```

95

```
T I F F S   S E W E R   H I M
A V A I L   P E A L E   U M A
C A R D I N A L S I N   D E C
K N E E P A D S   E S S A Y
  L U G E   L E G I O N S
S T R I P S   T A V E R N
L O O T S   F A C E D   H O W
A B B Y   M I X E R   F A K E
P E I   D A V I D   H O W I E
  N I E C E S   B O O K E D
P A L A C E S   F I S T
A R E N A   O A K T R E E S
S E A   D O U B L E E A G L E
T A C   E A S E L   S C A L E
A S H   S T A Y S   S E D A N
```

96

```
A L I A S   T H U S   C H A
M A N G O   D I A N E   R O W
O N C E I N A L I F E T I M E
E G O S   O M E G A   A M E S
B E D   C N N   I N D I G O
A R E T H A   P O R E   N A M
  H O M E R S   S H A M E
  T W I C E T O L D T A L E
G H E N T   A D O R E S
L A S   A L L S   A G H A S T
O T T A W A   P I G   B A H
A C E D   P L A I N   C O N E
T H R E E T I M E S A L A D Y
E E L   R O V E R   B A R E R
D R Y   A P E X   A N D R E
```

97

```
S E N T U P   B U L K H E A D
A T E A S E   A L A N A L D A
T H E G O O D H U M O R M A N
W E D   S N O   A W L
I L L S   S O F A   O H M E
T W E A K   M A R K T W A I N
H A S T E N   L I E U   I D O
  T H E B A D L A N D E R S
M E A   A M O S   T O R R E S
M R R O B E R T S   R I A N T
E S P N   S O U P   N I T A
  D O G   L A O   S E G
T H E U G L Y D U C K L I N G
M U S T R E A D   T R A N C E
C H E Y E N N E   S A N G E R
```

98

```
B I N G O   J I L T   T B A R
A D O R N   O R E O   O A H U
R O G E T   K I S S   S C A M
B L O W O N E S S T A C K
  P E R   A D A G E S
C M A J O R   F D A   A N T
L E T O F F S T E A M   M C I
E M M Y   E A R   C M O N
R O O   P O P O N E S C O R K
I R S   O U T   D I S N E Y
C Y P R U S   S I M
H I T T H E C E I L I N G
A L E C   I O W A   L O S E R
B A R K   N L E R   A L B E E
E X E S   G E R E   R A N D Y
```

99

```
A M A S S   B O G I E   D A M
P U T U P   I T A L Y   I D O
E M E R A L D I S L E   A M A
  F R I E S   G A M I N
C A R A T S   B A L L O T S
E D U C A T E   A G A I N
R O B E   S T O R E S   D O S
T R Y S T   H I T   S A B R E
S E T   A N A L O G   L A T E
  U N I O N   K A R A C H I
T H E A L P S   R E C K O N
H O S T S   B O T H A
E N D   P E A R L H A R B O R
I D A   I V I E D   S T O N E
R A Y   N E R D S   H E X E D
```

100

```
A B I T · U N H I P · U S S R
L A D E · N O O S E · P H I L
B R E A K I N G I N · S A P S
A R A R A T · · S A Y I N · ·
N Y L O N · · · L O D G E S ·
· · F E W E S T · · D E R A T
B O F F · E X C U S E · I R A
R U E · W E I R D A L · L T R
I T E · O P T I O N · A A H S
C E L L O · S P R E A D · · ·
K R I L L S · · · H O S T S ·
· · N O S E S · T A R T A N ·
E D G Y · R E M E M B E R M E
M O O D · G A U G E · R I P E
I N K S · E N D O N · S P A R
```

101

```
P R O · B A S E H I T · S T S
L A X · A M E R I C A · M O P
A N N A N I C O L E S M I T H
S C A L D · T O T · T O R T E
M I R I A M · · U E C K E R ·
A D D · G A P · L P S · I R E
· · A E R A T E S · S E E S ·
· C I N D Y C R A W F O R D ·
· R A N T · K A I S E R S · ·
E D U · H A S · E P I · S D S
B I N N E Y · · T S H I R T ·
E L D E R · H U E · K E N Y A
C L A U D I A S C H I F F E R
C A T · E T H I C A L · U S E
A C E · D E N N E H Y · L T D
```

102

```
I N G A · D E F C O N · J A B
F U E L · I L L I N I · A G O
S T A G I N G A R E A · F I X
O S R I C · · T C I · K A L E
· S E C R E T A D M I R E R ·
L A H R · E L O · A O L · · ·
S W I S S A L P S · P O W E R
A E F · C P I · A S U · H B O
T E T R A · S E X A P P E A L
· · A R F · N O R · E E N Y ·
S T U F F E D A N I M A L · ·
C O P T · N O M · · O R B I T
O K S · S N O O Z E A L A R M
L Y E · H E D R E N · E S M E
D O T · E L Y S E E · D E A N
```

103

```
C L A S S Y · A D A M S A L E
R E C I T E · R E L A P S E D
A N O D E S · G E T G O I N G
S T R E E T R O D · G R A Z E
H O N A L E E · S U I T · · ·
· · · I R M A · P E S T E R ·
B L A S E · A F R O · B O N E
R I L L · T I T A N · A D Z E
I L S A · A L O T · B R O O K
M Y O P I C · N E H I · · · ·
· · · S M O G · D O G S T A R
S L A T E · N O R T H P O L E
P A P I L L O N · T O R R I D
A N E C D O T E · E R A S E D
D A R K A G E S · A N T O N Y
```

104

```
C A S H · H A D O N · A S P S
A L O U · O P E R A · T H E O
T A N G E R I N E S · T R A Y
E I G H T D A Y S A W E E K ·
· · · T E N · · · I N V · · ·
D O G M A S · F I E L D E R S
A C R E · U L N A E · P O I ·
W H E N I M S I X T Y F O U R
E R A · G A S E S · · U R G E
S E T T L E R S · E A R T H S
· · S A O · · · A D M · · · ·
· O C T O P U S S G A R D E N
T R O T · S T A Y A T H O M E
V E T O · S A V O R · E L M O
S O T O · T H E U S · A L A N
```

105

```
C A L · T A I L P I N · A P T
U N O · A R M O I R E · T O W
I N D E X F I N G E R · E L I
S U G G E S T · O N T · L E N
I L I A D · C U E S T I C K
N U N N · F O O T · H E A L ·
E S G · B R A N · S P O R T Y
· · · D R A F T B E E R · · ·
A R M O R Y · A L A N · C H I
L E A P · A C T S · B L O T ·
F A C E L I F T · T O U T S ·
A D A · A S L · B O R S C H T
L O B · P L A C E K I C K E R
F U R · S A M A R I A · E A U
A T E · E M E R G E D · D D E
```

106

```
H A N G · G A T O · M A H R E
O M A R · W R A P · A L O U D
N O V A · A N T E · L I M N S
D E E P G R E E N P A G E S ·
A B L E R · · · I C Y · S I T
S A S · A L E R T S · C O N K
· · S M I T E · A L I T O · ·
P A Y M U D B U F F A L O · ·
· · C O M F Y · U S U R P · ·
E S P Y · A N S A R I · F D S
E T H · A T A · · C A I R N ·
· P I N K M I M O S A · M A Y O
D U B A I · L A V A · M S R P
U N I V S · E X E C · A C U E
O K A Y S · D I R K · N O B S
```

107

```
M A D E · H I P · · T E R R I
T W I N · U P A T · U S A I N
V E S T · S E T H · N A I V E
· S C R A T C H A N D S N I P
C O P Y R O A S T E R · B E T
A M A · E N C · T W A · O R L
L E D O N · F O E · S W A Y ·
· · I T I S T O L A P · · · ·
W E I L · S O D · F A B E R ·
O M G · A I S · T A L · A P E
L I N · C A U G H T A W H I P
F R O M T H E R A P T O R S ·
C A B I N · M I L L · N A T S
U T E R O · E L I A · K I L O
B E L O W · L A Y · A N E W
```

108

```
I M A M S · V E R B · A T M S
N O T I T · I L I A · S W A P
D U A L A C T I O N · T I T O
E S L · R O A N · G A R N E T
X Y L I T O L · D A M U P · ·
· · · V E T · N E W S D E S K
S I T A R · C A C A O · A P E
T O W N · M U R K Y · S K I P
I T O · L A R K S · W A S N T
R A T T A I L S · F E Y · · ·
· I M P L Y · P A S S K E Y
D E M I S E · L A I T · O D E
O P E N · D O U B L E D O W N
P E R U · I N X S · N I P I T
Y E S S · N E E T · D E A N A
```

109

```
I D E S T   C H O   S E A L S
M A T C H   H U H   P A L A U
A N T H O L O G Y   A S T I N
C L U M S Y C H E F   Y O R K
      O E D     S L O W
N I T E   I W O   A N I M A L
I D A   H A N D Y V A N I T Y
N I L L A   B O A   I S A A C
J O K E Y F A R M E R   T I E
A M S T E L   S S A   D A L E
      S K I T     T W O
D I O R   P A P A B A R B E R
A G G I E   S T A Y S S A N E
F O R D S   E U R   P U D G E
T R E E S   R I P   S M U R F
```

110

```
M R T   L A D I D A   B A L I
O U I   I M O N I T   U P O N
P B J C R E W C A T A L O G S
    A U R A   O N E I L L
A D A Y   I S L A N D   O R R
R U N   I M H O   D A D G U M
P B A P A P E R S   R Y E S
    E L S E   T A T A
P A P P   P B R R A T I N G
D O R E M I   A U T O   C U E
A L E   E N A C T S   P A A R
    S O N A T A   F I N N
P B S I S F O R S I L E N C E
S O O N   E N D U R O   O E R
Y A N K   W E I N E R   T D S
```

111

```
H O D   M C D L   K N O W S
S A N I T A R I A   R A D O N
P R E D A T O R Y   A N D R E
A D H O M I N E M   F A L S E
R C A   E L K   E X T   Y E R
K A N T   D I D N T W E
I N D I C A T E   C E L I A C
E D E M A   E B B   R I N N A
R Y D E R S   B A L K E D A T
    I D S A Y N O   L E A S
S O P   T A L   D U D   E L F
C U R E R   L O A D E D D I E
A T A R I   U N I T P R I C E
M E D I C   R A D I O E D I T
P R A N K   E S S E   D O A
```

112

```
W N B A   P A U L   C I T E D
H O U R   U R S A   H O H U M
O B S C E N E S T E A L E R S
O A T   S C A R   C R A B
S K E T C H   T O O   R P M
H E R E   U H A U L   B A R E
    R A P O B S E S S I O N
L E A R N   L Y S   O I N G O
O B L O N G I S L A N D
L A H R   R E S E T   E A V E
O N A   A E R   S Y S T E M
    M A R C   B R I E   T R I
T U B A L O B L I G A T I O N
B A R R E   L E O N   A R N E
S W A P S   T U T S   B E A M
```

113

```
R I B S   O N C E   V O T E S
O N L Y A T E S T   A D U L T
Y O U R B R A I N   M A R I O
A N N   B A R   A S P   O H M
L E T G O   A S T I C K U P
    E T H A N   U R I
J U S T T O S A Y   E T H E R
A R C H   E C L A T   A B L E
I L I E D   H O W W E D O I T
    L I P   G L A R E
J E O P A R D Y   R L E S S
U F C   R O N   C P A   R A T
I R A N I   A N O U T R A G E
C O L E S   S P I N A L T A P
E N A C T   E R N S   S O N S
```

114

```
A T M O S T   S A G   C O C K
S E A M U S   P H O   A S H E
H A H A H A   A M T   S P U N
    H A R D H A T H A R R Y
N E A R   I N D I A   E R A
W E S   T A S   S P Y O N
H I P H O P H O O R A Y
A N N A   P I N K S   R C M P
    H O S T E S S H O H O S
B L I N D   I S A   I M P
Y A N   O W I N G   Y M C A
H U N G R Y H U N G R Y
A R E A   N E E   H I P P O S
L I E S   N A V   I D E A L S
F E D S   E R E   J E T S E T
```

115

```
G A B E   M I A S M A   M R T
I D O S   B O L E Y N   O E R
G U Y T O E N A I L S   A L I
S E D E R   A N K A   S T Y X
    F E Y   O R E O
I N C A S E O F   B U D S
S O O N   C R O W D B R E A K
L U C   A C A C I A S   R C A
E N O U G H L U C K   B E R T
  S A G E   S K A T E K E Y
    L E G S   R Y E
Z A N Y   R E B A   P R A D A
I R E   L O V E C O O K I E S
N I X   E V E N E R   E D N A
C A T   S E N T R A   G A S P
```

116

```
E R I K   W O K S   S M U R F
L I D O   E D I T   S E N O R
H E Y D I D D L E D I D D L E
I N L A N D   O R E   I O L E
    K L E E   N C A A
R F D   A D A M   A S K F O R
O H O H   T T O P   T I L D E
Y O Y O C O M P E T I T I O N
A L E P H   E U R O   S E R E
L E N S E S   P E P S   S S W
    C R U Z   S N U G
O T R O   L A S   O C E A N S
W H A T S U P W I T H T H A T
L A N C E   P A R C   I S P Y
S I G H T   A N K H   N O S E
```

117

```
H U G E   G E N T   A G R E E
A R I L   A V O W   X R A Y S
L I M O   F I F I   E A S E L
L A M P O F L U X U R Y
S H E E N   T N T S   A G A S
    S P E W   S P R I T E
A P T   A D I O S   E E L E R
B L I M P O N T H E R A D A R
D A F O E   S O A M I   A M A
U N F U R L   K I W I
L O S S   E S M E   I N L A Y
    S P E N D I N G C A M P
A T W A R   A C T E   A M O R
D R A K E   I C U S   S I N E
J U D A S   L I P S   H A G S
```

118

```
OPED IEST AIMED
CLXI DYER FLYAT
TAPE AERIALISTS
ATOUCHOFGROUT
VER HON LAMINA
ESTEE ABET QED
MAJORED LUCE
COMPUTERGREEK
MANY GOATEED
SRI RUES RAZOR
TROWEL GAI EPA
NOPAINNOGRAIN
INDOORPOOL ELAL
NEILS ONME GOTO
COPSE DEER STEW
```

119

```
ELAL IAMBS RAZZ
SARA FLORA EPEE
SPECIALCAY LARS
ASCENT KNEWALOT
YEAST AUDREY
OWEPOSITIVE
HEAP EOS REDIG
ALBUMEN VIDALIA
HELGA SIC MEIN
AVENUEQUEUE
ANNULS TBSPS
MUSCADET UTOPIA
ASTI SEASTUDENT
NEAT INNIE ECCE
EDGY TSARS SKED
```

120

```
ACDC PESOS TULL
SHOR CAPRA OHIO
PAPERTRAIL YULE
CREDOS ROADSHOW
ADDIN WELDER
TAPEMEASURE
JOBS APE KSTAR
AMA DDT BUS ERA
YALEU ORR SSNS
RIBBONCANDY
BYROTE INUSE
SANTAANA REEVES
TROI TAGYOUREIT
RETD EMOTE GAZE
SAVE SENDS YSER
```

121

```
ASEA DONUT ASOF
DENT RAISA UNDO
DUSTBUSTER TOIL
TSUNAMIS PLOWED
OSE MSS ROOST
SAO TENN RAE
SUET LSAT GUARD
PLAYBOYMAGAZINE
UNSER REPO INON
RAT ICUS ORS
ENDUP CDE VAL
CAREER SOBSTORY
AFEW FUNNYPAGES
TAGS EVADE BUCO
ORGY WAGES SEAL
```

122

```
LINK BLINI AJAR
ERIE OASES SURE
WATERWHEEL KLEE
DESPAIR EASYAS
ONE PUTOFF
PAWNS RAS KOOKY
AMI OSAGES RUNE
NAN MEMENTO REA
ETDS MABELL TET
LIFER DOT DAHLS
LEEWAY RVS
TOOKTO SUITSUP
ROWE KINGSCROSS
APER ETATS OUTS
SSRS NOTSO SLAT
```

123

```
CHIEF CALF SRAS
RUNTO UTIL HAVA
OSCAR PLEA IBID
CHRISTIANSYMBOL
LAUDS HOMINY
LET KTS EMME
IMAGE LEO RHEA
MIXANIMALBREEDS
BRIT DOG ADAGE
EMIT PIP PEA
DIECUT ALBUM
ANGRYANDANNOYED
TARA ROOT ZLOTY
EWES OGRE ETHAN
SETH DOES LOOSE
```

124

```
ACMES SAKS BIDS
BOAST IDEA UNIT
ORDER CRYCRYCRY
MFA OGEE ROURKE
BUMPBUMPBUMP
EEE UMA WAS
ETNA SPEC NTEST
SHAKESHAKESHAKE
PRISM ATOM ERST
YUL BBS ERR
MOREMOREMORE
UNMADE AMYS LUV
BYEBYEBYE EXILE
ESTE ZING NIVEN
REAL ETTA TIERS
```

125

```
PSI ESTOPS SKAT
OPS SNOCAP TIRE
REO CIRCLEDANCE
SAGA FSU WINGS
CROSSFIRE ANTIC
HENLEY XAMOUNT
EDSEL SKED TEN
WAVEFRONT
FEH PACT AUSSI
FLYPAST TINTED
FEDON SQUAREONE
KRIEG APB ROSA
STARWITNESS LOM
ARNO RADNER IRA
WATT LEADTO ESP
```